D1134726

GROUND WATER

A Selected Bibliography

Frits van der Leeden is a consulting hydrogeologist and a senior member of the professional staff of Geraghty and Miller, Inc., a consulting firm specializing in ground-water studies. His work has taken him all over the United States and to many other parts of the world, where he has evaluated ground-water resources and supervised development of water supplies for industries, municipalities and governmental agencies.

Mr. van der Leeden has had extensive experience in large regional water resource investigations and in the compilation and evaluation of basic water information for all parts of the world. Among his other accomplishments, he is co-author of the Water Information Center's comprehensive *Water Atlas of the U. S.*

The Water Information Center is extremely pleased to publish this practical and concise work . . . a bibliography compiled and edited by someone actively working in the field of ground-water resources.

Fred L. Troise
Director of Publications

GROUND WATER
A Selected Bibliography

Compiled and edited by

Frits van der Leeden

Consulting Hydrogeologist
Geraghty & Miller, Inc.
Port Washington, N. Y.

WATER INFORMATION CENTER
WATER RESEARCH BUILDING
MANHASSET ISLE
PORT WASHINGTON, N. Y.

Set in Cold-type Composition and Designed by: *Trotta Composition, Inc.*
Printed and Bound by: *The Maple Press Company*

FOREWORD

In the United States, as well as elsewhere in the world, ground-water resources are being developed on an ever-increasing scale. More and more public, industrial, and private water supplies depend on ground water, and this resource now accounts for more than twenty percent of all fresh water withdrawn in our nation. All indications are that the development of ground-water resources will continue at a rapid pace. The science of hydrogeology is now being taught in many universities, and an increasing number of trained specialists in this field are joining federal, state and county organizations, private industry and consulting firms.

As a professional hydrogeologist, the compiler and other members of his organization have long felt a need for a handy, selected bibliographic reference to publications in the ground-water field. Because there has been a rapid increase in the last decade in the number of scientific articles and publications concerning hydrogeology, it is becoming an almost impossible task to keep track of all interesting and important papers. Moreover, there is a constant need, especially in report writing, to refer back to certain "classic" contributions in the field, and a quick reference guide along these lines should be quite helpful.

With the foregoing uses in mind, this bibliography of selected important papers has been prepared. Most papers concerning local hydrogeologic conditions have been omitted, except in certain cases where the contents were considered to be of more encompassing value. The guide purposely has been kept as simple as possible. The approximately 1,500 references it contains have been listed under 32 topics, each dealing with a particular aspect of the field of ground-water hydrology. Each reference is listed only once, alphabetically by author. References that are themselves bibliographies dealing with specific topics such as artificial recharge, water law, etc., are listed under those headings. A section for general bibliographies is also included.

It is sincerely hoped that this publication will serve as a useful contribution to the growing need for information about the important natural resource of ground water. Comments and suggestions for improvement of the bibliography will be welcomed.

Westbury, New York *Frits van der Leeden*
May 1971

CONTENTS

	Page
FOREWORD	v
BOOKS	1
JOURNALS AND BULLETINS	4
HISTORY AND DEVELOPMENT OF GROUND-WATER HYDROLOGY	5
GENERAL BIBLIOGRAPHIES	6
GROUND-WATER ENVIRONMENTS	8
EXPLORATION TECHNIQUES, MAPPING AND DATA COLLECTION	11
GEOPHYSICAL PROSPECTING	14
WELL LOGGING	20
HYDRAULIC CHARACTERISTICS OF AQUIFERS	22
WATER LEVELS AND FLUCTUATIONS	25
SPRINGS AND GEOTHERMAL RESOURCES	29
THEORY OF GROUND-WATER FLOW	32
PUMPING TESTS AND FIELD OBSERVATIONS	44
TRACERS	48
CHEMICAL QUALITY AND WATER STANDARDS	50
	58

		Page
CONTAMINATION OF GROUND WATER		58
RADIONUCLIDES IN GROUND WATER		62
SALT-WATER INTRUSION		65
WELL DESIGN AND DRILLING METHODS		71
WELL MAINTENANCE AND STIMULATION		75
PUMPING EQUIPMENT		76
ARTIFICIAL RECHARGE, RIVER INFILTRATION AND STORAGE		77
SUBSURFACE DISPOSAL		88
BASIN STUDIES AND WATER BALANCES		90
PHREATOPHYTES AND EVAPOTRANSPIRATION		95
BASE FLOW AND BANK STORAGE		96
GROUND-WATER MODELS		98
LAND SUBSIDENCE		105
GROUND-WATER LAW		108
MANAGEMENT AND CONSERVATION		110
EDUCATION AND TRAINING		115
WATER WITCHING		116

GROUND WATER

A Selected Bibliography

BOOKS

AGADJANOV, A. M., 1950, *Hydrogeology and Hydraulics of Ground Water and Oil* (in Russian), Gostoptekhizdat, Moscow, 280 pp.

AMERICAN SOCIETY OF CIVIL ENGINEERS, 1949, *Hydrology Handbook*, Manual of Engineering Practice 28, New York, 184 pp.

ANDERSON, K. E., (ed.), 1963, *Water Well Handbook*, Missouri Water Well Drillers Assoc., Rolla, Mo., 281 pp.

BENITEZ, ALBERTO, 1963, *Captación de aguas subterráneas*, Editorial Dossat, Madrid, 157 pp.

BOGOMOLOV, G. V. and SILIN-BEKCURIN, A. I., 1955, *Special Hydrogeology* (in Russian), Gosgeoltekhizdat, Moscow, 247 pp., transl. into French by E. Jayet and G. Castany, Service d'Information Géol., 1959, Paris, 235 pp.

BOGOMOLOV, G. V., 1957, *Grundlagen der Hydrogeologie*, Deutscher Verl. der Wissenschaften, Berlin, 187 pp.

BOGOMOLOV, G. V., 1965, *Hydrogéologie*, Transl. from Russian by V. Frolov, Libr. du Globe, Paris, 277 pp.

BUTLER, S. S., 1957, *Engineering Hydrology*, Prentice-Hall, Inc., Englewood Cliffs, N. J.

CASTANY, GILBERT, 1963, *Traité pratique des eaux souterraines*, Dunod, Paris, 657 pp.

CASTANY, GILBERT, 1967, *Prospection et exploitation des eaux souterraines*, Dunod, Paris.

CEDERGREN, H. R., 1967, *Seepage, Drainage and Flow Nets*, John Wiley & Sons, Inc., New York.

CHILDS, E. C., 1969, *Introduction to the Physical Basis of Soil Water Phenomena*, John Wiley & Sons, Inc., New York.

DACHLER, R., 1936, *Grundwasserströmung*, J. Springer, Vienna, 141 pp.

DAVIS, S. N. and DE WIEST, R. J. M., 1966, *Hydrogeology*, John Wiley & Sons, Inc., New York.

DE WIEST, R. J. M., 1965, *Geohydrology,* John Wiley & Sons, Inc., New York.

DE WIEST, R. J. M., (ed), 1969, *Flow through Porous Media,* Academic Press, New York, 530 pp.

ERIKSSON, E. and others, 1968, *Ground Water Problems,* Pergamon Press, Inc., Elmsford, N. Y., Oxford, England.

FLEMMING, H. W., 1962, *Die unterirdische Wasserspeicherung,* Oldenburg Ver., Munich, 79 pp.

FORCHHEIMER, P., 1930, *Hydraulik,* B. G. Teubner Verlagsgesellschaft, Berlin.

FOURMARIER, P., 1958, *Hydrogéologie,* 2nd ed., Paris, Masson & Cie., 294 pp.

HARR, M. E., 1962, *Ground Water and Seepage,* McGraw-Hill Book Co., Inc., New York, 315 pp.

HEILAND, C. A., 1946, *Geophysical Exploration,* Prentice-Hall Inc., New York, 1013 pp.

IMBEAUX, E., 1930, *Essai d'hydrogéologie,* Dunod, Paris, 704 pp.

INGERSOLL, L. R. and others, 1948, *Heat Conduction with Engineering and Geological Applications,* McGraw-Hill Book Co., Inc., New York.

JOHNSON, EDWARD E., INC., 1966, *Ground Water and Wells,* St. Paul, Minn., 440 pp.

KARR, W. V., 1969, *Ground Water: Methods of Extraction and Construction,* Internat. Underground Water Inst., Bexley, Ohio.

KAZMANN, R. G., 1965, *Modern Hydrology,* Harper & Row, Inc., New York, 301 pp.

KEILHACK, K., 1935, *Lehrbuch der Grundwasser- und Quellenkunde,* 3rd ed., Gebr. Borntraeger, Berlin, 575 pp.

KOEHNE, W., 1928, *Grundwasserkunde,* E. Nagele, Stuttgart, 291 pp.

KUENEN, P. H., 1963, *Realms of Water,* John Wiley & Sons, Inc., New York, 327 pp.

LINSLEY, R. K., Jr., and others, 1958, *Hydrology for Engineers,* McGraw-Hill Book Co. Inc., New York.

McGUINNESS, C. L., 1963, *The Role of Ground Water in the National Water Situation,* U. S. Geol. Survey Water Supply Paper 1800, 1121 pp.

MEINZER, O. E., (ed.), 1942, *Hydrology*, McGraw-Hill Book Co., Inc., New York, 712 pp.

MILLER, D. W. and others, 1963, *Water Atlas of the United States — Basic Facts about the Nation's Water Resources*, Water Information Center, Port Washington, N. Y. (3rd ed. in preparation).

OGIL'VI, N. A. and FEDOROVICH, D. I., 1966, *Groundwater Seepage Rates*, Plenum Publ. Corp., New York.

PFANNKUCH, H. O., 1969, *Dictionary of Hydrogeology*, (Eng., Fr., Ger.), Am. Elsevier Publ. Co., Inc., New York.

POLUBARINOVA-KOCHINA, P. Ya., 1962, *Theory of Ground-Water Movement*, Princeton Univ. Press, Princeton, N. J., 613 pp.

PLOTNIKOV, N. A., 1962, *Ressources en eaux souterraines: classification et méthodes d'évaluation*, transl. from Russian by M. Laronde, Gauthier-Villars, Paris, 194 pp.

PRINZ, E., 1923, *Handbuch der Hydrologie*, 2nd ed., J. Springer, Berlin, 422 pp.

RAU, JOHN, 1970, *Ground Water Hydrology for Water Well Drilling Contractors*, Natl. Water Well Assoc., Columbus, Ohio.

SCHNEEBELZ, T., 1966, *Hydraulique souterraine*, Eyrolles, Paris.

SCHOELLER, R. H., 1962, *Les eaux souterraines*, Masson, Paris, 642 pp.

SILIN-BEKCURIN, A. I., 1961, *Hydrogeology of Irrigated Lands*, Foreign Languages Publ. House, Moscow, 110 pp.

THOMAS, H. E., 1951, *The Conservation of Ground Water*, McGraw-Hill Book Co., Inc., New York, 327 pp.

TODD, D. K., 1959, *Ground Water Hydrology*, John Wiley & Sons, Inc., New York, 336 pp.

TODD, D. K., 1970, *The Water Encyclopedia*, Chap. 4, Ground Water, Water Information Center, Port Washington, N. Y., pp. 186-218.

TOLMAN, C. F., 1937, *Ground Water*, McGraw-Hill Book Co., Inc., New York, 593 pp.

U. S. CONGRESS, 1955, *Water* (The Yearbook of Agriculture), 84th Cong., 1st sess., 751 pp.

VEN TE CHOW, (ed.), 1964, *Handbook of Applied Hydrology*, McGraw-Hill Book Co., Inc., New York.

VERRIJUT, A., 1970, *Theory of Ground Water Flow,* Gordon & Breach, Inc., New York.

WALTON, W. C., 1970, *Groundwater Resource Evaluation,* McGraw-Hill Book Co., Inc., 664 pp.

WISLER, C. O. and BRATER, E. F., 1959, *Hydrology,* John Wiley & Sons, Inc., New York.

JOURNALS AND BULLETINS

AGUA — Centro de Estudios, Investigacion y Aplicaciones del Agua, Paseo de San Juan 39, Barcelona 9, Spain.

AMERICAN SOCIETY OF CIVIL ENGINEERS, HYDRAULICS DIVISION JOURNAL — Am. Soc. Civil Engrs., 345 East 47th St., New York, N. Y. 10017.

AMERICAN SOCIETY OF CIVIL ENGINEERS, IRRIGATION AND DRAINAGE DIVISION JOURNAL, Am. Soc. Civil Engrs., 2500 South State St., Ann Arbor, Mich. 48104.

AMERICAN SOCIETY OF CIVIL ENGINEERS, SANITARY ENGINEER-ING DIVISION JOURNAL, Am. Soc. Civil Engrs., 2500 South State St., Ann Arbor, Mich. 48104.

BULLETIN OF THE AMERICAN ASSOCIATION OF PETROLEUM GEOLOGISTS — Am. Assoc. Petroleum Geol., P. O. Box 979, Tulsa, Okla. 74101.

BULLETIN DU BUREAU DE RECHERCHES GEOLOGIQUES ET MINIERES — Paris.

BULLETIN INTERNATIONAL ASSOCIATION OF SCIENTIFIC HY-DROLOGY — Internat. Assoc. Sci. Hydrology, Gontrode Heirweg 45H, Melle (Post Merlebeke), Belgium.

EOS — Transactions Am. Geophys. Union, 2100 Pennsylvania Ave. N. W., Washington, D. C. 20037.

GEOLOGICAL SOCIETY OF AMERICA BULLETIN — Geol. Soc. Am., P. O. Box 1719, Boulder, Colo. 80302.

GROUND WATER — Tech. Div. Nat. Water Well Assoc., P. O. Box 222, Urbana, Ill. 61801.

GROUND WATER AGE — 92 Martling Ave., Tarrytown, New York, N. Y. 10591.

HYDATA — Bibliographic references published by the Am. Water Resources Assoc., P. O. Box 434, Urbana, Ill. 61801.

JOURNAL AMERICAN WATER WORKS ASSOCIATION — Am. Water Works Assoc., 2 Park Ave., New York, N. Y. 10016.

JOURNAL NEW ENGLAND WATER WORKS ASSOCIATION — New England Water Works Assoc., 726 Statler Office Bldg., Boston, Mass. 02116.

JOURNAL OF GEOPHYSICAL RESEARCH — Am. Geophys. Union., 2100 Pennsylvania Ave. N. W., Washington, D. C. 20037.

JOURNAL OF HYDROLOGY   North-Holland Publishing Co., Postbox 3489, Amsterdam, The Netherlands.

SOVIET HYDROLOGY: SELECTED PAPERS — Am. Geophys. Union, 2100 Pennsylvania Ave. N. W., Washington, D. C. 20037.

UOP JOHNSON DRILLERS JOURNAL — UOP Johnson Div., 315 North Pierce St., St. Paul, Minn. 55104.

WATER RESOURCES BULLETIN — Am. Water Resources Assoc., P. O. Box 434, Urbana, Ill. 61801.

WATER RESOURCES RESEARCH — Am. Geophys. Union, 2100 Pennsylvania Ave. N. W., Washington, D. C. 20037.

WATER WELL JOURNAL — Water Well Journal Publ. Co., Box 222, Urbana, Ill. 61801.

HISTORY AND DEVELOPMENT OF
GROUND-WATER HYDROLOGY

ADAMS, F. D., 1928, *Origin of Springs and Rivers — a Historical Review,* Fennia, v. 50, no. 1, 16 pp.

ARISTOTLE, *Meteorologica,* translated by E. W. Webster, in W. D. Ross (ed.), The Oxford Translation of the Complete Works of Aristotle, 1923-1955, v. 3, Clarendon Press, Oxford.

BAKER, M. N., and HORTON, R. E., 1936, *Historical Development of Ideas Regarding the Origin of Springs and Ground Water,* Trans. Am. Geophys. Union, v. 17, pp. 395-400.

BISWAS, A. K., 1970, *History of Hydrology,* American Elsevier Publ. Co., Inc., New York, 336 pp.

FERRIS, J. G. and SAYRE, A. N., 1955, *The Quantitative Approach to Groundwater Investigations,* Economic Geology, 50th anniversary volume.

HALL, H. P., 1954, *A Historical Review of Investigations of Seepage toward Wells,* J. Boston Soc. Civil Engrs., July, pp. 251-311.

JONES, P. B. and others, 1963, *The Development of the Science of Hydrology,* Texas Water Comm. Circ. 63-03, 35 pp.

MEINZER, O. E., 1934, *The History and Development of Ground-Water Hydrology,* J. Washington Acad. Sci., v. 24, pp. 6-32.

PALISSY, B., *Discours Admirables,* translated by A. LaRocque, The Admirable Discourses of Bernard Palissy, Univ. of Illinois Press, Urbana, Ill.

PARIZEK, R. R., 1963, *The Hydrologic Cycle Concept,* Mineral Ind. Penn. State Univ. v. 32, no. 7.

PERRAULT, PIERRE, 1967, *On the Origin of Springs,* Transl. by Aurele LaRocque, Hafner Publ. Co., New York, 209 pp.

GENERAL BIBLIOGRAPHIES

AMERICAN GEOPHYSICAL UNION, Washington, D. C.
1937, *Bibliography of Hydrology, United States of America for the Year 1935 and 1936,* 78 pp.
1938, *Bibliography of Hydrology, United States of America for the Year 1937,* 68 pp.
1939, *Bibliography of Hydrology of the United States of America for the Year 1938,* 72 pp.

AMERICAN GEOPHYSICAL UNION, Washington, D. C. (continued)
1940, *Bibliography of Hydrology of the United States for the Year 1939,* 86 pp.
1941, *Bibliography of Hydrology of the United States of America for the Year 1940,* 86 pp.

AMERICAN GEOPHYSICAL UNION, 1952, *Annotated Bibliography on Hydrology, 1941-1950 (United States and Canada),* Fed. Inter-Agency River Basin Comm., Subcomm. on Hydrology, Notes on Hydrologic Activities Bull. 5, 408 pp.

AMERICAN GEOPHYSICAL UNION, 1955, *Annotated Bibliography on Hydrology, 1951-54, and Sedimentation, 1950-54 (United States and Canada),* U. S. Inter-Agency Comm. Water Resources Joint Hydrology-Sedimentation Bull. 8, 207 pp.

BRADBURY, C. E. and others, 1964, *Annotated Bibliography on Hydrology and Sedimentation, 1959-1962 (United States and Canada),* U. S. Inter-Agency Comm. Water Resources Joint Hydrology — Sedimentation Bull. 8, 323 pp.

GIEFER, G. J. and TODD, D. K., 1971, *State Water Resources Publications,* Water Information Center, Port Washington, N. Y. (in preparation).

JOHNSON, A. I., 1964, *Selected Bibliography on Laboratory and Field Methods in Ground-Water Hydrology,* U. S. Geol. Survey Water Supply Paper 1779-Z.

MARGAT, JEAN, 1964, *Guide Bibliographique d'hydrogéologie;* ouvrages et articles en langue francaise, Bureau de Recherches Géologiques et Minières, suite Hydrogéologie 113, Paris.

RANDOLPH, J. R. and DEIKE, R. G., 1966, *Bibliography of Hydrology of the United States, 1963,* U. S. Geol. Survey Water Supply Paper 1863, 166 pp.

RIGGS, H. C., 1962, *Annotated Bibliography on Hydrology and Sedimentation, United States and Canada, 1955-58,* U. S. Geol. Survey Water-Supply Paper 1546, 236 pp.

U. S. GEOLOGICAL SURVEY, OFFICE OF INTERNATIONAL ACTIVITIES, 1967, *Interim Bibliography of Reports Related to Overseas Activities of the Water Resources Division, 1940-67,* Open file rept., 26 pp.

VORHIS, R. C., 1957, *Bibliography of Publications Relating to Ground Water Prepared by the Geological Survey and Cooperating Agencies 1946-55,* U. S. Geol. Survey Water Supply Paper 1492, 203 pp.

WARING, G. A., and MEINZER, O. E., 1947, *Bibliography and Index of Publications Relating to Ground Water Prepared by the Geological Survey and Cooperating Agencies,* U. S. Geol. Survey Water-Supply Paper 992, 412 pp.

WELLISCH, H., 1967, *An International Bibliography of Water Resources Development 1950-1965,* Israel Program for Sci. Transl. Jerusalem; also Daniel Davey & Co., Inc., New York

GROUND WATER ENVIRONMENTS

ABD-EL-AL, IBRAHIM, 1953, *Statics and Dynamics of Water in the Syro-Lebanese Limestone Massifs,* Proc. Ankara Symp. on Arid Zone Hydrology, pp 60-76, UNESCO, Paris.

ADAMS, W. M., 1969, *Geophysical Studies for Volcanological Geohydrology,* Hawaii Water Resources Res. Center Contrib. no. 18.

AMBROGGI, R. P., 1966, *Water under the Sahara,* Sci. Am., v. 214, no. 5, pp. 21-29.

BOGOMOLOV, G. V., 1961, *Conditions of Formation of Fresh Waters under Pressure in Certain Desert Zones of North Africa, the U. S. S. R., and South-West Asia,* in *Salinity Problems in the Arid Zones,* pp. 37-41, UNESCO, Paris.

BUCHAN, S., 1963, *Geology in Relation to Ground Water,* J. Inst. Water Engineers, v. 17, pp. 153-164.

BURDON, D. J., and PAPAKIS, N., 1962, *Handbook of Karst Hydrogeology,* United Nations Food and Agricultural Organization, Inst. for Sub-Surface Res., Athens.

BURDON, D. J., 1967, *Hydrogeology of Some Karstic Areas of Greece,* in *Hydrology of Fractured Rocks,* Proc. Dubrovnik Symp. Oct. 1965, Internat. Assoc. Sci. Hydrology, Pub. 73, pp. 308-317.

CEDERSTROM, D. J. and others, 1953, *Occurrence and Development of Ground Water in Perma-Frost Regions,* U. S. Geol. Survey Circ. 275, 30 pp.

DARTON, N. H., 1897, *Preliminary Report on Artesian Waters of a Portion of the Dakotas,* U. S. Geol. Survey 17th Ann. Rept. Part 2, pp. 1-92.

DAVIS, W. M., 1930, *Origin of Limestone Caverns,* Geol. Soc. Am. Bull., v. 41, pp. 475-628.

DESHPANDE, B. G., and SEN GUPTA, S. N., 1956, *Geology of Ground Water in the Deccan Traps and the Application of Geophysical Methods,* India Geol. Survey Bull., ser. B, no. 8, 22 pp.

ENSLIN, J. F., 1943, *Basins of Decomposition in Igneous Rocks, their Importance as Underground Water Reservoirs and their Location by the Electrical Resistivity Method,* Trans. Geol. Soc. South Africa, v. 46, pp. 1-12.

GEZÉ, B., 1965, *Les conditions hydrogéologiques des roches calcaires,* Chronique d'Hydrogéologie no. 7, pp. 9-39.

HOPKINS, D. M., and others, 1955, *Permafrost and Ground Water in Alaska,* U. S. Geol. Survey Prof. Paper 264-F, pp. 113-146.

HOWARD, A. D., 1963, *The Development of Karst Features,* Natl. Speleological Soc. Bull, v. 25, pp. 45-65.

HOWARD, A. D., 1964, *A Model for Cavern Development under Artesian Ground-Water Flow, with Special Reference to the Black Hills,* Bull. Natl. Speleol. Soc. v. 26, pp. 7-16.

INTERNATIONAL ASSOCIATION OF SCIENTIFIC HYDROLOGY, 1967, *Hydrology of Fractured Rocks,* Proc. Dubrovnik Symp., Oct. 1965.

KIERSCH, G. A., and HUGHES, P. W., 1952, *Structural Localization of Ground Water in Limestones – Big Bend District, Texas-Mexico,* Econ. Geol. v. 47, pp. 794-806.

KUNIN, V. V., 1957, *Conditions of the Formation of Underground Waters in Deserts,* Internat. Assoc. Sci. Hydrology, General Assembly Toronto, Pub. 44, v. 2, pp. 502-516.

LAMOREAUX, P. E. and others, 1970, *Hydrology of Limestone Terranes – Annotated Bibliography of Carbonate Rocks,* Geol. Survey Alabama, Bull. 94, Pt. A, 242 pp.

LAMOREAUX, P. E., and POWELL, W. J., 1960, *Stratigraphic and Structural Guides to the Development of Water Wells and Well Fields in a Limestone Terrane,* Internat. Assoc. Sci. Hydrology Pub. no. 52, pp. 363-375.

LATTMAN, L. H., and PARIZEK, R. R., 1964, *Relationship between Fracture Traces and the Occurrence of Ground Water in Carbonate Rocks,* J. Hydrology, v. 2, pp. 73-91.

LeGRAND, H. E., 1949, *Sheet Structure, a Major Factor in the Ocurrence of Ground Water in the Granites of Georgia,* Econ. Geol., v. 44, pp. 110-118.

MEINZER, O. E., 1959, *The Occurrence of Ground Water in the United States,* U. S. Geol. Survey Water Supply Paper 489.

MITHAL, R. S., and SINGHAL, B. B. S., (eds.), 1969, Proc. Symposium on *Ground Water Studies in Arid and Semiarid Regions,* Dept. of Geology and Geophysics, Univ. of Roorkee, Roorkee, India.

NEAL, J. T., 1969, *Playa Variation,* in McGinnies, W. G. and Goldman, B. J., *Arid Lands in Perspective,* University of Arizona Press, pp. 15-44.

NEWCOMB, R. C., 1959, *Some Preliminary Notes on the Ground Water of the Columbia River Basalt,* Northwest Sci., v. 33, pp. 1-18.

PICARD, L., 1953, *Outline of Ground-Water Geology in Arid Regions,* Proc. Ankara Symp. on Arid Zone Hydrology, pp. 165-176, UNESCO, Paris.

RADZITZKY, d'OSTROWICK, I., 1953, *L'hydrogéologie des roches calcareuses,* Dinant, L. Bordeaux-Capelle, 199 pp.

ROBAUX, A., 1953, *Physical and Chemical Properties of Ground Water in the Arid Countries,* Proc. Ankara Symp. on Arid Zone Hydrology, pp. 17-28, UNESCO, Paris.

STEARNS, H. T., 1946, *Geology and Ground-Water Resources of the Island of Hawaii,* Terr. Hawaii Div. Hydrography Bull. v. 9, 368 pp.

STEWART, J. W., 1962, *Relation of Permeability and Jointing in Crystalline Metamorphic Rocks near Jonesboro, Georgia,* U. S. Geol. Survey Prof. Paper 450-D, pp. 168-170.

STRINGFIELD, V. T. and LEGRAND, H. E., 1966, *Hydrology of Limestone Terranes in the Coastal Plain of the Southeastern United States,* Geol. Soc. Am. Spec. Paper 93, 46 pp.

TEMPERLEY, B. N., 1960, *A Study of the Movement of Groundwater in Lava-Covered Country,* Overseas Geol. and Mineral Resources, v. 8, pp. 37-52.

THEIS, C. V., 1965, *Ground Water in Southwestern Region,* in *Fluids in Subsurface Environments,* Am. Assoc. Petroleum Geol. Mem. 4, pp. 327-342.

THOMAS, H. E., 1952, *Ground-water Regions of the United States – their Storage Facilities,* in *The Physical and Economic Foundation of Natural Resources,* v. 3, House Interior and Insular Affairs Comm., U. S. Congress.

TISDEL, F. W., 1964, *Water Supply from Ground Water Sources in Permafrost Areas of Alaska,* in *Science in Alaska 1963,* 14th Alaskan Science Conference, Am. Assoc. Advancement of Sci., Alaska Div., pp. 113-124.

UNESCO, 1962, *The problems of the Arid Zone,* Proc. Paris Symp., Arid Zone Research 18, UNESCO, Paris, 481 pp.

WALTON, W. C. and SCUDDER, G. D., 1960, *Ground-Water Resources of the Valley-Train Deposits in the Fairborn Area, Ohio,* Ohio Div. Water, Tech. Rept. no. 3.

WHITE, W. B., 1969, *Conceptual Models for Carbonate Aquifers,* Ground Water, v. 7, no. 3, pp. 15-22.

WILLIAMS, J. R., 1965, *Ground Water in Permafrost Regions: An annotated Bibliography,* U. S. Geol. Survey Water Supply Paper 1792, 294 pp.

WILLIAMS, J. R., 1970, *Ground Water in the Permafrost Regions of Alaska,* U. S. Geol. Survey Prof. Paper 696.

WINQVIST, G., 1953, *Ground Water in Swedish Eskers,* Lindstahl, Stockholm, 91 pp.

EXPLORATION TECHNIQUES, MAPPING AND DATA COLLECTION

BENTAL, RAY, 1963, *Methods of Collecting and Interpreting Ground-Water Data,* U. S. Geol. Survey Water Supply Paper 1544-H.

BOGOMOLOV, G. V. and PLOTNIKOV, N. A., 1957, *Classification of Underground Water Resources and their Plotting on Maps,* Internat. Assoc. Sci. Hydrology, General Assembly Toronto, Pub. 44, v. 2, pp. 86-97.

CARTWRIGHT, KEROS, 1968, *Thermal Prospecting for Ground Water,* Water Resources Res. v. 4, no. 2, pp. 395-403.

CASTANY, GILBERT and MARGAT, JEAN, 1965, *Les cartes hydrologiques,* Internat. Assoc. Sci. Hydrology Bull., v. 10, no. 1, pp. 74-81.

CHURINOV, M. V., 1957, *Hydrogeological Maps and their Role in Estimating the Water-Bearing Capacity of Rocks and Subsoil Water Resources,* Internat. Assoc. Sci. Hydrology, Pub. 44, v. 2, pp. 62-67 (1958).

DaCOSTA, J. A., 1960, *Presentation of Hydrologic Data on Maps in the United States of America,* Internat. Assoc. Sci. Hydrology, Pub. 52, pp. 143-186.

DRACUP, J. A. and SHAPIRO, K. A., 1967, *Remote Sensing of Hydrologic Data by Satellites,* Proc. Third Ann. Conf. Am. Water Resources Assoc., San Francisco, Calif. pp. 472-484.

FENT, O. S., 1949, *Use of Geologic Methods in Ground-Water Prospecting,* J. Am. Water Works Assoc., v. 41, pp. 590-598.

HOWE, R. H. L. and others, 1956, *Application of Air Photo Interpretation in the Location of Ground Water,* J. Am. Water Works Assoc., v. 48, no. 11, pp. 1380-1390.

HOWE, R. H. L., 1960, *The Application of Aerial Photographic Interpretation to the Investigation of Hydrologic Problems,* Photogramm. Eng., v. 26, no. 1, pp. 85-95.

INTERNATIONAL ASSOCIATION OF SCIENTIFIC HYDROLOGY/ UNESCO/INSTITUTE OF GEOLOGICAL SCIENCES, 1970, *International Legend for Hydrogeological Maps,* (English/French/Spanish/ Russian), 101 pp.

JONES, N. E., 1966, *Bibliography of Remote Sensing of Resources,* U. S. Army Corps of Engrs., Ft. Belvoir, Va., for NASA, Earth Resources Program Office, N68-1 870, 40 pp.

LAYTON, J. P. (ed.), 1970, *Proceedings of the Princeton University Conference on Aerospace Methods for Revealing and Evaluating Earth's Resources,* Sept. 25-26, 1969, Princeton, N. J.

LEE, KENNAN, 1969, *Infrared Exploration for Shoreline Springs at Mono Lake, Californial Test Site,* Stanford Univ. Remote Sensing Lab., Tech. Rept. 69-7.

LEGGETTE, R. M., 1950, *Prospecting for Ground Water-Geologic Methods,* J. Am. Water Works Assoc. v. 42, pp. 945-946.

LEPLEY, L. K., and PALMER, L. A., 1967, *Remote Sensing of Hawaiian Coastal Springs Using Multispectral and Infrared Techniques,* Univ. of Hawaii Water Resources Res. Center Tech. Report 18.

LLAVERIAS, R. K., 1970, *Remote Sensing Bibliography for Earth Resources,* 1966-67, U. S. Geol. Survey, Clearinghouse Fed. Sci. and Tech. Inf., PB 192863, Springfield, Va.

LOHMAN, S. W., and ROBINOVE, C. J., 1964, *Photographic Description and Appraisal of Water Resources,* Photogrammetria, v. 19, no. 3, 1962-1964.

LOWE, R. H. and others, 1956, *Application of Air Photo Interpretation in the Location of Ground Water,* J. Am. Water Works Assoc., v. 48, p. 559, May.

MANN, J. F., JR., 1958, *Estimating Quantity and Quality of Ground Water in Dry Regions Using Airphotographs,* Internat. Assoc. Sci. Hydrology, General Assembly of Toronto, v. 2, pp. 125-134.

MARGAT, JEAN, 1966, *La cartographie hydrogéologique,* Bur. Rech. Geol. Min., Publ. no. DS 66A 130.

MAZLOUM, S., 1953, *Boring and Prospecting for Ground-Water in Arid Zones,* Proc. Ankara Symp. on Arid Zone Hydrology, pp. 184-187, UNESCO, Paris.

MCNELLIS, J. M. and others, 1968, *Digital Computer Applications that Facilitate Collection and Interpretation of Ground-Water Data,* Reprint from Tucson Symp., Dec. 1968, U. S. Geol. Survey Lawrence, Kans.

MEER, G. E., 1969, *Aerial Photographic Method for Studying Ground Water,* Army Foreign Sci. and Technology Center, Clearinghouse for Fed. Sci. and Tech. Info., Accession no. AD-690613, Springfield, Va.

MEINZER, O. E., 1927, *Plants as Indicators of Ground Water,* U. S. Geol. Survey Water Supply Paper 577, 95 pp.

MEYBOOM, P., 1961, *A Semantic Review of the Terminology of Ground-water Maps.* Bull. Internat. Assoc. Sci. Hydrology, v. 6, no. 1, pp. 29-36.

NEFEDOV, K. Ye., 1964, *Hydrogeologic Mapping by Means of Aerial-Photographic Survey Data,* Doklady Acad. Sciences USSR, Earth Sciences Section, Am. Geol. Institute, v. 148, pp. 90-92.

PETTYJOHN, W. A., and RANDICH, P. G., 1966, *Geohydrologic Use of Lithofacies Maps in Glaciated Areas,* Water Resources Res., Fourth Quarter, v. 2, no. 4, pp. 679-689.

PETTYJOHN, W. A., 1967, *Evaluation of Basic Data and a Variety of Techniques Needed in Hydrologic Systems Analysis,* in *System Approach to Water Quality in the Great Lakes,* Proc. Am. Symp. Water Resources Res., Ohio State Univ. Water Resource Center, 3d.

POWELL, W. J. and others, 1970, *Delineation of Linear Features and Application to Reservoir Engineering Using Apollo 9 Multispectral Photography,* Geol. Survey of Alabama, Inf. ser. 41.

ROBERTSON, C. E., 1963, *Well Data for Water Well Yield Map,* Missouri Geol. Survey and Water Resources, 23 pp.

ROBINOVE, C. J., 1965, *Infrared Photography and Imagery in Water Resources Research,* J. Am. Water Works Assoc., v. 57, no. 7, pp. 834-840.

STRANDBERG, C. H., 1967, *Color Aerial Photography for Water Supply and Pollution Control Reconnaissance,* Proc. Third Ann. Conf. on Remote Sensing of Air and Water Pollution, North Am. Aviation, Inc., Autonetics Div., Anaheim, Calif., pp. 13-1 to 13-10.

THORPE, T. W., 1950, *Prospecting for Ground Water-Test Drilling,* J. Am. Water Works Assoc., v. 42, pp. 957-960.

UNITED NATIONS WATER RESOURCES CENTER, 1960, *Large-Scale Ground-Water Development,* Pub. no. 60, II. B. 3, UNIPUB, Inc., New York, 84 pp.

UNITED STATES GEOLOGICAL SURVEY, 1968, *Bibliography of Remote Sensing of Earth Resources for Hydrological Applications 1960-1967,* U. S. Geol. Survey open-file Interagency rept. NASA-134.

WALTON, W. C., and NEILL, J. C., 1963, *Statistical Analysis of Specific-Capacity Data for a Dolomite Aquifer,* J. Geophys. Res., v. 68, pp. 2251-2262.

GEOPHYSICAL PROSPECTING

BARNES, H. E., 1952, *Soil Investigations Employing a New Method of Layer-Value Determination for Earth Resistivity Interpretation,* Highway Res. Bd. Bull. 65, pp. 26-36.

BAYS, C. A., 1950, *Prospecting for Ground Water—Geophysical Methods,* J. Am. Water Works Assoc., v. 42, pp. 947-956.

BAYS, C. A., and FOLK, S. H., 1944, *Developments in the Application of Geophysics to Ground-Water Problems,* Illinois Geol. Survey Circ. 108, 25 pp.

BERSON, I. S. and others, 1959, *Wave Refraction by Aquiferous Sands,* U. S. S. R. Acad. Sci. Bull., Geophysics Ser., Jan. and Feb. (English transl. by the Am. Geophys. Union), pp. 17-29 and pp. 115-118.

BONINI, W. E., 1959, *Seismic-Refraction Method in Ground-Water Exploration,* Trans. Am. Inst. Mining Metall. Engrs., v. 211, pp. 485-488.

BUHLE, M. B., 1953, *Earth Resistivity in Ground-Water Studies in Illinois,* Trans. Am. Inst. Mining Engrs., Tech. Paper 3496L, Mining Eng., pp. 395-399.

BURWELL, E. B., Jr., 1940, *Determination of Ground-Water Levels by the Seismic Method,* Trans. Am. Geophys. Union, v. 21, pp. 439-440.

CARTWRIGHT, K. and McCOMAS, M. R., 1968, *Geophysical Surveys in the Vicinity of Sanitary Landfills in Northeastern Illinois,* Ground Water, v. 6, no. 5, Sept.-Oct., pp. 23-31.

COMPAGNIE GENERALE DE GEOPHYSIQUE, 1963, *Master Curves for Electrical Sounding,* European Assoc. of Exploration Geophysicists.

CONWELL, C. N., 1951, *Application of the Electrical Resistivity Method to Delineation of Areas of Seepage Along a Canal—Wyoming Canal—Riverton Project,* Geol. Rep. G-114, U. S. Bureau Reclamation, Denver, Colo., 10 pp.

DIZIOGLU, M. Y., 1953, *Underground Water Investigations by Means of Geophysical Methods (Particularly Electrical) in Central Anatolia,* Proc. Ankara Symp. on Arid Zone Hydrology, UNESCO, Paris, pp. 199-215.

DUGUID, J. O., 1968, *Refraction Determination of Water Table Depth and Alluvium Thickness,* Geophysics, v. 33, no. 3 June.

FLATHE, H., 1955, *A Practical Method of Calculating Geoelectrical Model Graphs for Horizontally Stratified Media,* Geophys. Prospecting, v. 3, pp. 268-294.

FLATHE, H., 1963, *Five-Layer Master Curves for the Hydrogeological Interpretation of Geoelectrical Resistivity Measurements above a Two-Story Aquifer,* Geophys. Prospecting, v. 11, pp. 471-508.

FOSTER, J. W., and BUHLE, M. B., 1951, *An Integrated Geophysical and Geological Investigation of Aquifers in Glacial Drift near Champaign—Urbana, Illinois,* Econ. Geol., v. 46, pp. 368-397.

GISH, O. H., and ROONEY, W. J., 1925, *Measurement of Resistivity of Large Masses of Undisturbed Earth,* Terrestrial Magnetism, v. 30, no. 4, pp. 161-188.

HACKETT, J. E., 1956, *Relation between Earth Resistivity and Glacial Deposits near Shelbyville, Illinois,* Ill. State Geol. Survey Circ. 223.

HALL, D. H., and HAJUAL, Z, 1962, *The Gravimeter in Studies of Buried Valleys,* Geophysics, v. 27, no. 6, pt. 2, pp. 939-951.

HALLENBECK, F., 1953, *Geo-Electrical Problems of the Hydrology of West German Area,* Geophys. Prospecting, v. 1, pp. 241-249.

HEILAND, C. A., 1937, *Prospecting for Water with Geophysical Methods,* Trans. Am. Geophys. Union, v. 18, pp. 574-588.

JENKO, F., 1959, *The Hydrogeology and Water Economy of Karst,* Ljubljana, Državna Založba Slovenije, 237 p.

JOHNSON, R. B., 1954, *Use of the Refraction Seismic Method for Differentiating Pleistocene Deposits in the Arcola and Tuscola Quadrangles, Illinois,* Ill. State Geol. Survey Rept. Invest. 176.

JOINER, T. J., and SCARBROUGH, W. L., 1969, *Hydrology of Limestone Terranes – Geophysical Investigations,* Univ. of Alabama, Bull. 94, part D.

JONES, P. H., and Buford, T. B., 1951, *Electric Logging Applied to Groundwater Exploration,* Geophysics, v. 6, no. 1.

JONES, P. H., and SKIBITZKE, H. E., 1956, *Subsurface Geophysical Methods in Ground-Water Hydrology,* Advances in Geophys., v. 3, pp. 241-300.

KELLY, S. F., 1962, *Geophysical Exploration for Water by Electrical Resistivity,* J. New England Water Works Assoc., v. 76, pp. 118-189.

LANDES, K. K., and WILSON, J. T., 1943, *Ground-Water Exploration by Earth-Resistivity Methods,* Papers Mich. Acad. Arts, Sci., Let., v. 29, pp. 345-354.

LEE, F. W., 1936, *Geophysical Prospecting for Underground Waters in Desert Areas,* Inf. Circ. 6899, U. S. Bureau Mines, Washington, D. C., 27 pp.

LINEHAN, D., and KEITH, S., 1948, *Seismic Reconnaissance for Ground Water Development,* J. New England Water Works, Assoc., v. 63, no. 1.

LINEHAN, D., 1951, *Seismology Applied to Shallow Zone Research,* Am. Soc. Test. Materials, Spec. Tech. Pub. 122, pp. 156-170.

McDONALD, H. R., and WANTLAND, D., 1961, *Geophysical Procedures in Ground Water Study,* Trans. Am. Soc. Civil Engrs., v. 126.

McGINNIS, L. D., and KEMPTON, J. P., 1961, *Integrated Seismic, Resistivity, and Geologic Studies of Glacial Deposits,* Illinois Geol. Survey Circ. 323, 23 pp.

McGINNIS, L. D. and others, 1963, *Relationship of Gravity Anomalies to a Drift-Filled Bedrock Valley System in Northern Illinois,* Ill. State Geol. Survey Circ. 354, 23 pp.

MEINZER, O. E., 1937, *The Value of Geophysical Methods in Ground-Water Studies,* Trans. Am. Geophys. Union, v. 18, pp. 385-387.

MOONEY, H. M., and WETZEL, W. W., 1956, *The Potentials About a Point Electrode and Apparent Resistivity Curves for a Two-, Three-, and Four-Layered Earth,* Univ. Minn. Press, Minneapolis.

MOORE, R. W., 1957, *Applications of Electrical Resistivity Measurements to Subsurface Investigations,* Public Roads, v. 29, no. 7.

MORLEY, L. W. (ed.), 1969, *Mining and Groundwater Geophysics/1967,* Econ. Geol. Rept. 26, Dept. of Energy, Mines and Resources, Ottawa, Canada.

ORELLANA, ERNESTO, 1961, *Criterios erróneos en la interpretación de sondeos eléctricos:* Revista de Geofisica, v. 20, pp. 207-227.

ORELLANA, ERNESTO, and MOONEY, H. M., 1966, *Master Tables and Curves for Vertical Electrical Sounding over Layered Structures,* INTERCIENCIA, Madrid.

PAVER, G. L., 1945, *On the Application of the Electrical Resistivity Method of Geophysical Surveying to the Location of Underground Water, with Examples from the Middle East,* Proc. Geol. Soc. London, pp. 46-51, Apr.

PAVER, G. L., 1948, *Iso-Resistivity Mapping for the Investigation of Underground Water Supplies,* General Assembly Oslo, Internat. Assoc. Sci. Hydrology, v. 3, pp. 290-295.

PAVER, G. L., 1950, *The Geophysical Interpretation of Underground Water Supplies, a Geological Analysis of Observed Resistivity Data,* J. Inst. Water Engrs., v. 4, pp. 237-266.

PRICKETT, T. A. and others, 1964, *Groundwater Development in Several Areas of Northeastern Illinois,* Ill. State Water Survey Rept. of Invest. 47.

PRIDDY, R. R., 1955, *Fresh-Water Strata of Mississippi as Revealed by Electric Studies,* Miss. Geol. Survey Bull. 83.

ROBERTSHAW, J., and BROWN, P. D., 1955, *Geophysical Methods of Exploration and their Application to Civil Engineering Problems,* Proc. Inst. Civil Engrs., pt. 1, v. 4, pp. 644-690.

ROMAN, IRWIN, 1952, *Resistivity Reconnaissance,* Am. Soc. Testing Mater. Spec. Tech. Pub. 122.

SAYRE, A. N., and STEPHENSON, E. L., 1937, *The Use of Resistivity-Methods in the Location of Salt-Water Bodies in the El Paso, Texas Area,* Trans. Am. Geophys. Union, v. 18, pp. 393-398.

SHAW, S. H., 1963, *Some Aspects of Geophysical Surveying for Ground Water,* J. Inst. Water Engrs., London, v. 17, pp. 175-188.

SHEPARD, E. R., and WOOD, A. E., 1940, *Application of the Seismic Refraction Method of Subsurface Exploration to Flood-Control Projects,* Trans. Am. Inst. Min. and Met. Engrs., v. 138, pp. 312-325.

SMITH, W. O., and NICHOLS, H. B., 1953, *Mapping Water-Saturated Sediments by Sonic Methods,* Sci. Monthly, v. 77, no. 1, July.

SPANGLER, D. P., and LIBBY, F. J., 1968, *Application of the Gravity Survey Method to Watershed Hydrology,* Ground Water, v. 6, no. 6, pp. 21-27.

SPICER, H. C., 1952, *Electrical Resistivity Studies of Subsurface Conditions near Antigo, Wisconsin,* U. S. Geol. Survey Circ. 181, 19 pp.

STALLMAN, R. W., 1963, *Type Curves for the Solution of Single-Boundary Problems,* U. S. Geol. Survey Water Supply Paper 1545-C, pp. 45-47.

STICKEL, J. F., JR. and others, 1952, *Geophysics and Water,* J. Am. Water Works Assoc., v. 44, pp. 23-35.

SWARTZ, J. H., 1937, *Resistivity Studies of some Salt-Water Boundaries in the Hawaiian Islands,* Trans. Am. Geophys. Union, v. 18, pp. 387-393.

SWARTZ, J. H., 1939, *Geophysical Investigations in the Hawaiian Islands,* Trans. Am. Geophys. Union, v. 20, pp. 292-298.

TAGG, G. F., 1934, *Interpretation of Resistivity Measurements,* Trans. Am. Inst. Mining Met. Eng., Geophys. Prospecting, pp. 135-145.

TATTAM, C. M., 1937, *The Application of Electrical Resistivity Prospecting to Ground Water Problems,* Colorado School of Mines Quart., v. 32, pp. 117-138.

TODD, D. K., 1955, *Investigating Ground Water by Applied Geophysics,* Proc. Am. Soc. Civil Engrs., v. 81, 625, 14 pp.

VACQUIER, V. and others, 1956, *Prospecting for Ground Water by Induced Electrical Polarization,* New Mexico Inst. of Mining and Technology, Res. and Devel. Div., 41 pp.

VAN DAM, J. C., 1955, *Geo-Electrical Investigations in the Delta Area of the Netherlands,* Serv. for Water Resources Dev. (Rijkswaterstaat), The Netherlands.

VAN NOSTRAND, R. G., and COOK, K. L., 1966, *Interpretation of Resistivity Data,* U. S. Geol. Survey Prof. Paper 499, 310 pp.

VOLKER, ADRIAN, and VAN DAM, J. C., 1954, *Geo-elektrisch onderzoek bij uitvoering van waterbouwkundige werken,* Serv. for Water Resources Dev. (Rijkswaterstaat), The Netherlands.

VOLKER, A., and DIJKSTRA, J., 1955, *Détermination des salinités des eaux dans le sous-sol du Zuiderzee par prospection géophysique,* Geophys. Prospecting, v. 3, pp. 111-125.

WARNER, D., 1969, *Preliminary Field Studies Using Earth Resistivity Measurements for Delineating Zones of Contaminated Ground Water,* Ground Water, v. 7, no. 1.

WARRICK, R. E., and WINSLOW, J. D., 1960, *Application of Seismic Methods to a Ground-Water Problem in Northeastern Ohio,* Geophysics, v. 25, no. 2, pp. 505-519.

WAY, H. J. R., 1942, *An Analysis of the Results of Prospecting for Water in Uganda by the Resistivity Method,* Trans. Inst. Min. and Met. Engrs., v. 51, pp. 285-310.

WENNER, F., 1916, *A Method of Measuring Earth-Resistivity,* Bull. Bureau Standards, v. 12, Washington, D. C., pp. 469-478.

WETZEL, W. W., and McMURRY, H. V., 1937, *A Set of Curves to Assist in the Interpretation of the Three-Layer Resistivity Problem,* Geophysics, v. 2, pp. 329-341.

WILSON, G. V. and others, 1970, *Evaluation, by Test Drilling, of Geophysical Methods Used for Ground-Water Development in the Piedmont Area, Alabama,* Geol. Survey of Alabama Circ. 65, 15 pp.

WORKMAN, L. E., and LEIGHTON, M. M., 1937, *Search for Ground Water by the Electrical Resistivity Method,* Trans. Am. Geophys. Union, v. 18, pp. 403-409.

WOOLLARD, G. P., and HANSON, G. F., 1954, *Geophysical Methods Applied to Geologic Problems in Wisconsin,* Wisc. Geol. Survey Bull. 78, Sci. ser. 15.

WELL LOGGING

ANONYMOUS, 1951, *Interpretation Handbook for Resistivity Logs,* Doc. 4, Schlumberger Well Surveying Corp., Houston, Texas, 148 pp.

ARCHIE, G. E., 1942, *The Electrical Resistivity Log as an Aid in Determining some Reservoir Characteristics,* Trans. Am. Inst. Min. and Met. Engrs., v. 146, pp. 54-62.

BAFFA, J. J., 1948, *The Utilization of Electrical and Radio-Activity Methods of Well Logging for Ground-Water Supply Development,* J. New England Water Works Assoc., v. 62, pp. 207-219.

BARNES, B. A., and LIVINGSTON, P., 1947, *Value of the Electrical Log for Estimating Ground-Water Supplies and the Quality of Ground Water,* Trans. Am. Geophys. Union, v. 28, pp. 903-911.

BENNETT, R. R., and PATTEN, E. P., 1960, *Borehole Geophysical Methods for Analyzing Specific Capacity of Multi-Aquifer Wells,* U. S. Geol. Survey Water Supply Paper 1536-A, pp. 1-25.

BLANKENNAGEL, R. K., 1968, *Geophysical Logging and Hydraulic Testing, Pahute Mesa, Nevada Test Site,* Ground Water, v. 6, no. 4, pp. 24-32.

BRYAN, F. L., 1950, *Application of Electric Logging to Water Well Problems,* Water Well J., v. 4, no. 1, pp. 3-7.

DOLL, H. G., 1949, *The S. P. Log: Theoretical Analysis and Principles of Interpretation,* Trans. Am. Inst. Min. and Met. Engrs., v. 179, pp. 146-185.

ERICKSON, C. R., 1946, *Vertical Water Velocity in Deep Wells,* J. Am. Water Works Assoc., v. 38, pp. 1263-1272.

FIEDLER, A. G., 1928, *The Au Deep-Well Current Meter and its Use in the Roswell Artesian Basin, New Mexico,* U. S. Geol. Survey Water Supply Paper 596, pp. 24-32.

GUYOD, HUBERT, 1965, *Interpretation of Electric and Gamma Ray Logs in Water Wells,* Am. Geophys. Union, Tech. Paper, Mandrel Industries Inc., Houston, Texas.

JONES, P. H., and BUFORD, T. D., 1951, *Electrical Logging Applied to Ground-Water Exploration,* Geophysics, v. 16, no. 1.

KEYS, W. S., 1968, *Well Logging in Ground-Water Hydrology,* Ground Water, v. 6, no. 1, pp. 10-19.

KIRBY, M. E., 1954, *Improve Your Work with Drilling-Time Logs,* Johnson Drillers' J., v. 26, no. 6, pp. 6-7, 14.

LIVINGSTON, P. P., and LYNCH, W., 1937, *Methods of Locating Salt-Water Leaks in Water Wells,* U. S. Geol. Survey Water Supply Paper 796-A, 20 pp.

MAHER, J. C., 1959, *The Composite Interpretive Method of Logging Drill Cuttings,* Oklahoma Geol. Survey Guide Book 8, 48 pp.

McCARDELL, W. M. and others, 1953, *Origin of the Electric Potential Observed in Wells,* Trans. Am. Inst. Min. and Met. Engrs., v. 198, pp. 41-50.

MEYER, W. R., 1963, *Use of a Neutron Moisture Probe to Determine the Storage Coefficient of an Unconfined Aquifer,* U. S. Geol. Survey Prof. Paper 450-E, pp. 174-176.

MOUNCE, W. D., and RUST, Jr., W. M., 1945, *Natural Potentials in Well Logging,* Trans. Am. Inst. Min. and Met. Engrs., v. 164, pp. 288-294.

MYLANDER, H. A., 1953, *Oil-Field Techniques Used for Water-Well Drilling,* J. Am. Water Works Assoc., v. 45, pp. 764-772.

PATTEN, E. P., and BENNETT, G. D., 1963, *Application of Electrical and Radioactive Well Logging to Ground-Water Hydrology,* U. S. Geol. Survey Water Supply Paper 1544-D, 60 pp.

PETERSON, F. L., and LAO, CHESTER, 1970, *Electric Well Logging of Hawaiian Basaltic Aquifers,* Ground Water, v. 8, no. 2, pp. 11-19.

POLAND, J. F., and MORRISON, R. B., 1940, *An Electrical Resistivity Apparatus for Testing Well Waters,* Trans. Am. Geophys. Union, v. 21, pp. 35-46.

RAMACHANDAR RAO, M. B., 1953, *Self-Potential Anomalies due to Subsurface Water Flow at Garimenapenta, Madras State, India,* Min. Eng., v. 5, pp. 400-403.

RUSSELL, W. L., 1941, *Well Logging by Radioactivity,* Am. Assoc. Petroleum Geologists Bull., v. 25, pp. 1768-1788.

STRATTON, E. F., and FORD, R. D., 1951, *Electric Logging,* in *Subsurface Geologic Methods* (L. W. LeRoy, ed.) 2nd ed., Colorado School of Mines, Golden, pp. 364-392.

TEXAS AGRIC. and MECH. COLLEGE, 1946, *Well Logging Methods Conference,* Texas Eng. Exp. Sta. Bull. 93, College Station, 171 pp.

TURCAN, A. N., JR., 1962, *Estimating Water Quality from Electrical Logs,* U. S. Geol. Survey Prof. Paper 450-C, pp. 135-136.

WALSTROM, J. E., 1952, *The Quantitative Aspects of Electric Log Interpretation,* Trans. Am. Inst. Min. and Met. Engrs., v. 195, pp. 47-58.

WYLLIE, M. R. J., 1949, *Statistical Study of Accuracy of some Connate-Water Resistivity Determinations Made from Self-Potential Log Data,* Am. Assoc. Petroleum Geologists Bull., v. 33, 1892-1900.

WYLLIE, M. R. J., 1963, *The Fundamentals of Well Log Interpretation,* Academic Press, New York, 238 pp.

HYDRAULIC CHARACTERISTICS OF AQUIFERS

ATHY, L. F., 1930, *Density, Porosity, and Compaction of Sedimentary Rocks,* Am. Assoc. Petroleum Geologists Bull., v. 14, pp. 1-24.

BARBER, E. S., 1955, *Symposium on Permeability of Soils,* Am. Soc. Testing Materials, Spec. Pub. no. 163, 136 pp.

BEDINGER, M. S., 1961, *Relation Between Median Grain Size and Permeability in the Arkansas River Valley, Arkansas,* U. S. Geol. Survey Prof. Paper 424-C, pp. 31-32.

BOSAZZA, V. L., 1952, On *Storage of Water in Rocks in Situ,* Trans. Am. Geophys. Union, v. 33, pp. 42-48.

CHRISTIANSEN, J. E., 1944, *Effect of Entrapped Air Upon the Permeability of Soils,* Soil Sci., v. 58, pp. 355-365.

COHEN, P., 1963, *Specific-Yield and Particle-Size Relations of Quaternary Alluvium Humboldt River Valley, Nevada,* U. S. Geol. Survey Water Supply Paper 1669-M, 24 pp.

DE RIDDER, N. A. and WITT, K. E., 1965, *A Comparative Study on the Hydraulic Conductivity of Unconsolidated Sediments,* J. of Hydrology, v. 3, pp. 180-206.

DOS SANTOS, A. G., Jr., and YOUNGS, E. G., 1969, *A Study of the Specific Yield in Land-Drainage Situations,* J. of Hydrology, v. 8, no. 1, May.

FISHEL, V. C., 1935, *Further Tests of Permeability with Low Hydraulic Gradients,* Trans. Am. Geophys. Union, v. 16, pp. 499-503.

FISHEL, V. C., 1942, *Bibliography on Permeability and Laminar Flow,* U. S. Geol. Survey Water Supply Paper 887, pp. 20-50.

FRANZINI, J. B., 1951, *Porosity Factor for Case of Laminar Flow through Granular Media,* Trans. Am. Geophys. Union, v. 32, pp. 443-446.

FRASER, H. J., 1935, *Experimental Study of Porosity and Permeability of Clastic Sediments,* J. Geology, v. 43, pp. 910-1010.

GAITHER, ALFRED, 1953, *A Study of Porosity and Grain Relationships in Experimental Sands,* J. Sed. Petrology, v. 23, pp. 180-195.

GRATON, L. C., and FRASER, H. J., 1935, *Systematic Packing of Spheres with Particular Relation to Porosity and Permeability, and Experimental Study of the Porosity and Permeability of Clastic Sediments,* J. Geol. v. 43.

HAZEN, A., 1893, *Some Physical Properties of Sands and Gravels with Special Reference to Their Use in Filtration,* 24th Ann. Rept., Mass. State Bd. Health, Boston.

JOHNSON, A. I., 1967, *Specific Yield — Compilation of Specific Yields for Various Materials,* U. S. Geol. Survey Water Supply Paper 1662-D.

JONES, O. R., and SCHNEIDER, A. D., 1969, *Determining Specific Yield of the Ogallala Aquifer by the Neutron Method,* Water Resources Res., v. 5, no. 6, p. 1267.

KLINKENBERG, L. J., 1941, *The Permeability of Porous Media to Liquids and Gases,* Drilling and Production Practice, Am. Petroleum Inst., New York, pp. 200-214.

KRUMBEIN, W. C., and Monk, C, D., 1943, *Permeability as a Function of the Size Parameters of Unconsolidated Sand,* Am. Inst. Min. and Met. Engrs., Trans. Petroleum Div., v. 151, pp. 153-163.

LANGBEIN, W. B., 1959, *Water Yield and Reservoir Storage in the United States,* U. S. Geol. Survey Circ. 409.

MANGER, G. E., 1963, *Porosity and Bulk Density of Sedimentary Rocks,* U. S. Geol. Survey Bull., 1144-E, 55 pp.

MEINZER, O. E., 1928, *Compressibility and Elasticity of Artesian Aquifers,* Econ. Geol. v. 23, pp. 263-291.

MERCADO, A., and HALEVY, E., 1966, *Determining the Average Porosity and Permeability of a Stratified Aquifer with the Aid of Radioactive Tracers,* Water Resources Res., v. 2, no. 3, pp. 525-531.

MORRIS, D. A., and JOHNSON, A. I., 1967, *Summary of Hydrologic and Physical Properties of Rock and Soil Materials, as Analyzed by the Hydrologic Laboratory of the U. S. Geological Survey, 1948-60,* U. S. Geol. Survey Water Supply Paper 1839-D, 42 pp.

MURRAY, R. C., 1960, *Origin of Porosity in Carbonate Rocks,* J. Sed. Petrology, v. 30, pp. 59-84.

NORRIS, S. E., 1963, *Permeability of Glacial Till,* U. S. Geol. Survey Prof. Paper 450-E, pp. 150-151.

RAMSAHOYE, L. E., and LANG, S. M., 1961, *A simple Method for Determining Specific Yield from Pumping Tests,* U. S. Geol. Survey Water Supply Paper 1536-C.

RASMUSSEN, W. C., 1963, *Permeability and Storage of Heterogeneous Aquifers in the United States,* Internat. Assoc. Sci. Hydrology, Pub. 64, pp. 317-325.

RODE, A. A., 1955, *Hydraulic Properties of Soils and Rocks* (in Russian), Acad. Sci. USSR, Moscow, 131 p.

SAYRE, A. N., and SMITH, W. O., 1962, *Retention of Water in Silts and Sands,* U. S. Geol. Survey Prof. Paper 450-C.

SNOW, D. T., 1967, *Rock Fracture Spacings, Openings and Porosities,* Am. Soc. Civil Engrs., Seattle Meeting Conf., Preprint 515, 42 pp.

STEARNS, N. D., 1928, *Laboratory Tests on Physical Properties of Water-Bearing Materials,* U. S. Geol. Survey Water Supply Paper 596, pp. 121-176.

TICKELL, F. G., and HIATT, W. N., 1938, *Effect of Angularity of Grain on Porosity and Permeability of Unconsolidated Sands,* Am. Assoc. Petroleum Geologists Bull., v. 22, pp. 1272-1279.

WATER LEVELS AND FLUCTUATIONS

BLANCHARD, F. B., and BYERLY, P., 1935, *A Study of a Well Gauge as a Seismograph,* Seismological Soc. Am. Bull., v. 25, pp. 313-321.

BLOEMEN, G. W., 1968, *Determination of Constant Rate Deep Recharge or Discharge from Ground-Water Level Data,* J. Hydrology, v. 6, no. 1, Jan.

BREDEHOEFT, J. D., 1967, *Response of Well-Aquifer Systems to Earth Tides,* J. Geophys. Res., v. 72, no. 12, pp. 3075-3087.

CARR, P. A., and VAN DER KAMP, G. S., 1969, *Determining Aquifer Characteristics by the Tidal Method,* Water Resources Res., v. 5, no. 5, p. 1023.

COOPER, H. H. and others, 1965, *The Response of Well-Aquifer Systems to Seismic Waves,* J. Geophys. Res., v. 70, pp. 3915-3926.

Da COSTA, J. A., 1964, *Effect of Hebgen Lake Earthquake on Water Levels in Wells in the United States,* U. S. Geol. Survey Prof. Paper 435-o, pp. 167-178.

FERRIS, J. G., 1951, *Cyclic Fluctuations of Water Level as a Basis for Determining Aquifer Transmissibility,* General Assembly Brussels, Internat. Assoc. Sci. Hydrology, Pub. 33, v. 2, pp. 148-155.

FISHEL, V. C., 1956 *Long-Term Trends of Ground-Water Levels in the United States,* Trans. Am. Geophys. Union, v. 37, pp. 429-435.

FRANKE, O. L., 1968, *Double-Mass Curve Analysis of the Effects of Sewering on Ground-Water Levels on Long Island, New York,* U. S. Geol. Survey Research 1968, Prof. Paper 600-B, pp. B205-209.

GARBER, M. S., and WOLLITZ, L. E., 1969, *Measuring Underground-Explosion Effects on Water Levels in Surrounding Aquifers,* Ground Water, v. 7, no. 4.

GEORGE, W. O., and ROMBERG, F. E., 1951, *Tide-Producing Forces and Artesian Pressures,* Trans. Am. Geophys. Union, v. 32, pp. 369-371.

GRANTZ, A. and others, 1964, *Alaska's Good Friday Earthquake, March 27, 1964, a Preliminary Geologic Evaluation,* U. S. Geol. Survey Circ. 491, 35 pp.

GUYTON, W. F., 1958, *Fluctuations of Water Levels and Artesian Pressure in Wells in the United States: their Measurement and Interpretation,* Internat. Assoc. Sci. Hydrology, General Assembly Oslo, Pub. 31, v. 3, pp. 85-92.

JACOB, C. E., 1939, *Fluctuations in Artesian Pressure Produced by Passing Railroad Trains as Shown in a Well on Long Island, New York,* Trans. Am. Geophys. Union, v. 20, pp. 666-674.

JACOB, C. E., 1943, *Correlation of Ground-Water Levels and Precipitation on Long Island, New York,* Trans. Am. Geophys. Union, v. 24, pp. 564-573.

JACOB, C. E., 1944, *Correlation of Ground-Water Levels and Precipitation on Long Island, New York,* Trans. Am. Geophys. Union, v. 25, pp. 928-939.

JACOB, C. E., 1945, *Correlation of Groundwater Levels and Precipitation on Long Island, N. Y.,* New York Dept. Conserv. Water Power and Control Comm. Bull. GW-14.

KOHOUT, F. A., 1961, *Fluctuations of Ground-Water Levels Caused by Dispersion of Salts,* J. Geophys. Res., v. 66, pp. 2429-2434.

La ROCQUE, G. A. Jr., 1941, *Fluctuations of Water Level in Wells in the Los Angeles Basin, California, during Five Strong Earthquakes, 1933-1940,* Trans. Am. Geophys. Union, v. 22, pp. 374-386.

LEWIS, M. R., 1932, *Flow of Ground-Water as Applied to Drainage Wells,* Trans. Am. Soc. Civil Engrs., v. 96, pp. 1194-1211.

LUSCZYNSKI, N. J., 1952, *The Recovery of Ground-Water Levels in Brooklyn, N. Y. from 1947 to 1950,* U. S. Geol. Survey Circ. 167, 29 pp.

MAASLAND, M., 1959, *Water-table Fluctuations Induced by Intermittent Recharge,* J. Geophys. Res., v. 64, pp. 549-559.

MAUCHA, L., and SARVARY, I., 1970, *Tidal Phenomena in the Karstic Water Level,* Bull. Internat. Assoc. Sci. Hydrology, v. 15, no. 2, June.

MEYER, A. F., 1960, *Effect of Temperature on Ground-Water Levels,* J. Geophys. Res., v. 65, pp. 1747-1752.

NETHERLANDS STATE INSTITUTE FOR WATER SUPPLY, 1948, *The Effect of the Yearly Fluctuations in Rainfall on the Flow of Ground Water from an Extended Area of Recharge,* General Assembly Oslo, Internat. Assoc. Sci. Hydrology, v. 3, pp. 47-56.

PARKER, G. G., and STRINGFIELD, V. T., 1950, *Effects of Earthquakes, Trains, Tides, Winds, and Atmospheric Pressure Changes on Water in the Geologic Formations of Southern Florida,* Econ. Geol., v. 45.

PECK, A. J., 1960, *The Water Table as Affected by Atmospheric Pressure,* J. of Geophys. Res., v. 65, no. 8.

PIPER, A. M., 1933, *Fluctuations of Water-Surface in Observation-Wells and at Stream Gaging-stations in the Mokelumne Area, California, during the Earthquake of December 20, 1932,* Trans. Am. Geophys. Union, v. 14, pp. 471-475.

REMSON, I., and RANDOLPH, J. R., 1958, *Application of Statistical Methods to the Analysis of Ground-Water Levels,* Trans. Am. Geophys. Union, v. 39, no. 1.

RICHARDSON, R. M., 1956, *Tidal Fluctuations of Water Level Observed in Wells in East Tennessee,* Trans. Am. Geophys. Union, v. 37, pp. 461-462.

RIGGS, H. C., 1953, *A Method of Forecasting Low Flow of Streams,* Trans. Am. Geophys. Union, v. 34, pp. 427-434.

ROBERTS, W. J., and ROMINE, H. E., 1947, *Effect of Train Loading on the Water Level in a Deep Glacial-Drift Well in Central Illinois,* Trans. Am. Geophys. Union, v. 28, pp. 912-917.

ROBINSON, T. W., 1939, *Earth-Tides Shown by Fluctuations of Water-Levels in Wells in New Mexico and Iowa,* Trans. Am. Geophys. Union, v. 20.

RORABAUGH, M. I., 1956, *Prediction of Ground-Water Levels on Basis of Rainfall and Temperature Correlations,* Trans. Am. Geophys. Union, v. 37, pp. 436-441.

ROSE, N. A., and ALEXANDER, Jr., W. H., 1945, *Relation of Phenomenal Rise of Water Levels to a Defective Gas Well, Harris County, Texas,* Bull. Am. Assoc. Petroleum Geologists, v. 29, pp. 253-279.

SOKOL, DANIEL, 1963, *Position and Fluctuations of Water Level in Wells Perforated in more than one Aquifer,* J. of Geophys. Res., v. 68, no. 4.

STALLMAN, R. W., 1955, *Numerical Analysis of Regional Water Levels to Define Aquifer Hydrology* (abstract), Trans. Am. Geophys. Union, v. 36, no. 3.

STALLMAN, R. W., 1956, *Numerical Analysis of Regional Water Levels to Define Aquifer Hydrology,* Trans. Am. Geophys. Union, v. 37, no. 4.

STALLMAN, R. W., 1961, *Relation Between Storage Changes at the Water Table and Observed Water-Level Changes*, U. S. Geol. Surv. Prof. Paper 424B, pp. 39-40.

STALLMAN, R. W., 1965, *Effects of Water-Table Conditions on Water-Level Changes near Pumping Wells*, Water Resources Res., v. 1, no. 2.

STEGGEWENTZ, J. H., 1933, *De invloed van de getijbeweging van zeeen en getijrivieren op de stijghoogte van grondwater*, thesis, Technische Hogeschool, Delft, The Netherlands.

STEWART, J. W., 1961, *Tidal Fluctuations of Water Levels in Wells in Crystalline Rocks in North Georgia*, U. S. Geol. Survey Prof. Paper 424-B, pp. 107-109.

THOMAS, H. E., 1940, *Fluctuations of Ground-Water Levels During the Earthquakes of November 10, 1938 and January 24, 1939*, Bull. Seismological Soc. Am., v. 30, pp. 93-97.

TROUSDELL, K. B., and HOOVER, M. D., 1955, *A Change in Ground-Water Level after Clearcutting of Loblolly Pine in the Coastal Plain*, J. Forestry, v. 53, pp. 493-498.

TROXELL, H. C., 1936, *The Diurnal Fluctuation in the Ground-Water and Flow of the Santa Ana River and its Meaning*, Trans. Am. Geophys. Union, v. 17, pp. 496-504.

TUINZAAD, H., 1954, *Influence of the Atmospheric Pressure on the Head of Artesian Water and Phreatic Water*, General Assembly Rome, Internat. Assoc. Sci. Hydrology, v. 2, pp. 32-37.

VEATCH, A. C., 1906, *Fluctuations of the Water Level in Wells, with Special Reference to Long Island, New York*, U. S. Geol. Survey Water Supply Paper 155, 83 pp.

VORHIS, R. C., 1955, *Interpretation of Hydrologic Data Resulting from Earthquakes*, Geol. Rundschau, v. 43.

VORHIS, R. C., 1964, *Earthquake-Induced Water-Level Fluctuations from a Well in Dawson County, Georgia*, Seismological Soc. Am Bull., v. 54, pp. 1023-1133.

WENZEL, L. K., 1936, *Several Methods of Studying Fluctuations of Ground-Water Levels*, Trans. Am. Geophys. Union, v. 17, pp. 400-405.

WERNER, P. W., 1946, *Notes on Flow-Time Effects in the Great Artesian Aquifers of the Earth*, Trans. Am. Geophys. Union, v. 27, pp. 687-708.

WERNER, P. W., and NOREN, D., 1951, *Progressive Waves in Nonartesian Aquifers,* Trans. Am. Geophys. Union, v. 32, pp. 238-244.

WHITE, W. N., 1932, *A Method of Estimating Ground-Water Supplies Based on Discharge by Plants and Evaporation from Soil,* U. S. Geol. Survey Water Supply Paper 659, pp. 1-105.

WILLIAMSON, R. E., and CARREKER, J. R., 1970, *Effect of Water-Table Levels on Evapotranspiration and Crop Yield,* Trans. Am. Soc. Agr. Engrs., v. 13, no. 2, Mar.-Apr.

WINOGRAD, I. J., 1970, *Noninstrumental Factors Affecting Measurement of Static Water Levels in Deeply Buried Aquifers and Aquitards, Nevada Test Site,* Ground Water, v. 8, no. 2, pp. 19-29.

ZONES, C. P., 1957, *Changes in Hydraulic Conditions in the Dixie Valley Areas, Nevada, After the Earthquake of December 16, 1954,* Seismological Soc. Am. Bull., v. 47, pp. 387-396.

SPRINGS AND GEOTHERMAL RESOURCES

BAKER, C. H., Jr., 1968, *Thermal Springs near Midway, Utah,* U. S. Geol. Survey Prof. Paper 600-D, pp. 63-70.

BENSEMAN, R. F., 1959, *Subsurface Discharge from Thermal Springs,* J. Geophys. Res., v. 64, no. 8.

BRYAN, K., 1919, *Classification of Springs,* J. Geol., v. 27, pp. 522-561.

BURDON, D. J., and SAFADI, C., 1963, *Ras-el-Ain: The Great Karst Spring of Mesopotamia, an Hydrogeologic Study,* J. Hydrology, v. 1, pp. 58-95.

CALIFORNIA DEPT. OF CONSERVATION, DIV. OF MINES AND GEOLOGY, 1965, *California Laws for Conservation of Geothermal Energy.*

CALIFORNIA DEPT. OF CONSERVATION, DIV. OF MINES AND GEOLOGY, 1966, *Geothermal Resources in California,* Mineral Inf. Service, v. 20, no. 7, June.

CALIFORNIA DEPT. OF CONSERVATION, DIV. OF MINES AND GEOLOGY, 1968, *Geothermal Resources,* Mineral Inf. Service, v. 21, no. 2, Feb.

CALIFORNIA DEPT. OF WATER RESOURCES, 1967, *Investigation of Geothermal Waters in the Long Valley Area, Mono County,* Office Rept., July.

CALIFORNIA DEPT. OF WATER RESOURCES, 1970, *Geothermal Wastes and the Water Resources of the Salton Sea Area,* Bull. 143-7, 126 pp.

CALIFORNIA LEGISLATURE, 1967, *Geothermal Resources – Foundation for a Potentially Significant New Industry in California,* Senate Permanent Fact Finding Comm., 4th Progress Rept., Regular Session.

CALIFORNIA LEGISLATURE, 1967, *Senate Bill No. 169* – Geothermal resources legislation.

CRAIG, H., 1966, *Isotopic Composition and Origin of the Red Sea and Salton Sea Geothermal Brines,* Sci., v. 154, no. 3756.

CRAIG, H., 1969, *Discussion – Source Fluids for the Salton Sea Geothermal System,* J. Am. Sci., v. 267, Feb.

FISHER, W. A. and others, 1966, *Freshwater Springs of Hawaii from Infrared Images,* U. S. Geol. Survey, Hydrologic Atlas 218.

HELGESON, H. C., 1968, *Geologic and Thermodynamic Characteristics of The Salton Sea Geothermal System,* J. Am. Sci., v. 266.

HEMLEY, J. J., 1967, *Aqueous Solutions and Hydrothermal Activity,* Trans. Am. Geophys. Union, v. 48, no. 2, June.

KOENIG, J. B., 1969, *Geothermal Exploration in the Western United States,* United Nations Symp. on Development and Utilization of Geothermal Resources, New York.

MANN, J. A., and CHERRY, R. N., 1970, *Large Springs of Florida's "Sun Coast" – Citrus and Hernando Counties,* Bureau of Geology, Florida Dept. of Nat. Resources, Tallahassee, Leaflet No. 9.

McNITT, J. R., 1960, *Geothermal Power,* Calif. Div. Mines Info. Serv., v. 13, no. 3.

McNITT, J. R., 1968, *Worldwide Development of Geothermal Industry,* Symp. Geothermal Resources, Am. Assoc. Petroleum Geologists, Bakersfield, Calif., March.

MEINZER, O. E., 1927, *Large Springs in the United States,* U. S. Geol. Survey Water Supply Paper 557, 94 pp.

MERCADO, G. S., 1960, *Aspectos quimicos del aprovechamiento de la energia geotermico, Campo Cerro Prieto B. C.,* Com. Federal Electricidad y Com. Energia Geotermica de Mexico, Mexicali, B. C., Oct.

MERCADO, G. S., 1969, *Cerro Prieto Geothermal Field, Baja California, Mexico,* Com. Energia Geotermico, Trans. Am. Geophys. Union, EOS v. 50, no. 2, Feb.

PRINZ, E., and KAMPE, R., 1934, *Handbuch der Hydrologie, Band II: Quellen,* J. Springer, Berlin, 290 pp.

RANDALL, W. and others, 1968, *Electrical Resistivity and Geochemistry of Aquifers in the Durmid Dome, Imperial Valley,* Trans. Am. Geophys. Union, v. 49, no. 4, Abstracts, Dec.

REX, R. W., 1966, *Heat Flow in the Imperial Valley of California,* Trans. Am. Geophys. Union, v. 47, no. 1, Abstracts.

REX, R. W., 1968, *Geochemical Water Facies in the Imperial Valley of California,* Trans. Am. Geophys. Union, v. 49, no. 4, Abstracts, Dec.

REX, R. W., 1968, *Investigation of the Geothermal Potential of the Lower Colorado River Basin, Phase 1 – The Imperial Valley Project,* Inst. of Geophysics and Planetary Physics, Univ. of California, Riverside, Calif. Oct. 30.

SABINS, F. F., 1967, *Infrared Imagery and Geologic Aspects, Indio Hills,* Photogrammetric Eng., July.

STEARNS, N. D. and others, 1937, *Thermal Springs in the United States,* U. S. Geol. Survey Water Supply Paper 679-B, pp. 59-191.

SUN, P-C. P. and others, 1963, *Large Springs of East Tennessee,* U. S. Geol. Survey Water Supply Paper 1755, 52 pp.

UNITED NATIONS, 1964, *Geothermal Energy,* Proc. Conf. New Sources of Energy, Rome, v. 2 and 3, Aug.

WARING, G. A., 1951, *Summary of Literature on Thermal Springs,* General Assembly Brussels, Internat. Assoc. Sci. Hydrology, v. 2, pp. 289-293.

WARING, G. A. revised by BLANKENSHIP, R. R. and BENTALL, RAY, 1965, *Thermal Springs of the United States and other Countries of the World – A Summary,* U. S. Geol. Survey Prof. Paper 492, 383 pp.

WHITE, D. E., and BRANNOCK, W. W., 1950, *The Sources of Heat and Water Supply of Thermal Springs, with Particular Reference to Steamboat Springs, Nevada,* Trans. Am. Geophys. Union, v. 31, pp. 566-574.

WHITE, D. E. 1957, *Thermal Waters of Volcanic Origin,* Bull. Geol. Soc. Am., v. 68, pp. 1637-1658.

WHITE, D. E. and others, 1963, *Geothermal Brine Well: Mile-Deep Drill Hole May Tap Ore-Bearing Magmatic Water and Rocks Undergoing Metamorphism,* Sci. v. 139, pp. 919-922.

THEORY OF GROUND WATER FLOW

AHMED, NAZEER and SUNADA, D. K., 1969, *Nonlinear Flow in Porous Media,* J. Hydraulics Div. Am. Soc. Civil Engrs., v. 95, no. HY 6, Nov.

AMERICAN PETROLEUM INSTITUTE, 1957, *Microscopic Behavior of Fluids in Porous Systems,* API Res. Proj. 47b, Dallas, Texas.

ARAVIN, V. I., and NUMEROV, S. N., 1953, *Theory of Fluid Flow in Undeformable Porous Media,* Jerusalem, Israel Program for Sci. Transl., 1965. (Russian original published in Moscow).

AVERY, S. B., 1953, *Analysis of Ground-Water Lowering Adjacent to Open Water,* Trans. Am. Soc. Civil Engrs., v. 118, pp. 178-208.

BABBITT, H. E., and CALDWELL, D. H., 1948, *The Free Surface Around,* and *the Interference Between, Gravity Wells,* Univ. Illinois Eng. Exp. Sta. Bull. 374, v. 45, no. 30, 60 pp.

BAKHMETEFF, B. A., and FEODOROFF, N. V., 1937, *Flow Through Granular Media,* J. Appl. Mech., v. 4A, p. 97 – Discussion, v. 5A, also 1937, pp. 86-90.

BALDWIN, G. V., and McGUINESS, C. L., 1963, *A Primer on Ground Water,* U. S. Geol. Survey, 26 pp.

BEAR, J. and others, 1968, *Physical Principles of Water Percolation and Seepage,* Arid Zone Research, v. 29, UNIPUB, Inc., New York.

BIANCHI, W. C., and HASKELL, Jr., E. E., 1966, *Air in the Vadose Zone as it Affects Water Movements beneath a Recharge Basin,* Water Resources Res., v. 2, no. 2, pp. 315-322.

BOKHARI, S. M. H. and others, 1968, *Drawdowns due to Pumping from Strip Aquifers,* J. Irrig. and Drainage Div., Am. Soc. Civil Engrs., v. 94, no. IR2, June.

BORELI, M., 1955, *Free-Surface Flow toward Partially Penetrating Wells,* Trans. Am. Geophys. Union, v. 36, pp. 664-672.

BOULTON, N. S., 1951, *The Flow Pattern near a Gravity Well in a Uniform Water-Bearing Medium,* J. Inst. Civil Engrs., v. 10.

BOULTON, N. S., 1954, *Unsteady Radial Flow to a Pumped Well Allowing for Delayed Yield from Storage,* Internat. Assoc. Sci. Hydrology, Gen. Assembly Rome, v. 2, Pub. 37.

BROWNELL, L. E., and KATZ, D. L., 1947, *Flow of Fluids through Porous Media, I — Single Homogeneous Fluids,* Chem. Eng. Progress, v. 43, pp. 537-548.

BRUTSAERT, W. and others, 1961, *Predicted and Experimental Water Table Drawdown during Tile Drainage,* Hilgardia, v. 31, pp. 389-418, Nov.

CASAGRANDE, A., 1937 and 1940, *Seepage through Dams,* J. New England Water Works Assoc., June 1937, also J. of Boston Soc. Civ. Engrs. 1940, pp. 295-337.

CHILDS, E. C., 1945, *The Water Table, Equipotentials, and Streamlines in Drained Land,* Soil Sci., v. 59.

COOPER, H. H., Jr., 1966, *The Equation of Groundwater Flow in Fixed and Deforming Coordinates,* J. Geophys. Res., v. 71, no. 20.

DAGAN, G., 1967, *A Method of Determining the Permeability and Effective Porosity of Unconfined Anisotropic Aquifers,* Water Resources Res., v. 3, no. 4, pp. 1059-1071.

DARCY, HENRI, 1856, *Les fontaines publiques de la Ville de Dijon,* Dalmont, Paris.

DE GLEE, G. J., 1930, *Over grondwaterstroomingen bij water-onttrekking door middel van putten,* J. Waltman Jr., Delft, 175 pp.

DE JONG, G. DE JOSSELIN, 1958, *Longitudinal and Transverse Diffusion in Granular Deposits,* Trans. Am. Geophys. Union, v. 39, pp. 67-74.

DE WIEST, R. J. M., 1961, *On the Theory of Leaky Aquifers,* J. Geophys. Res. v. 66, pp. 4257-4262.

DE WIEST, R. J. M., 1962, *Free Surface Flow in Homogeneous Porous Medium,* Trans. Am. Soc. Civil Engrs., v. 127, pt. 1, pp. 1045-1089.

DE WIEST, R. J. M., 1963, *Flow to an Eccentric Well in a Leaky Circular Aquifer with Varied Lateral Replenishment,* Geofisica Pura e Aplicata, v. 54, pp. 87-102.

DE WIEST, R. J. M., 1963, *Russian Contributions to the Theory of Ground-Water Flow,* Ground Water v. 1, no. 1, pp. 44-48.

DE WIEST, R. J. M., 1964, *History of the Dupuit-Forchheimer Assumptions in Ground-Water Flow*, Paper presented at the Annual Winter Meeting of the Am Soc. of Agric. Engrs., Dec., New Orleans.

DE WIEST, R. J. M., 1966, *On the Storage Coefficient and the Equations of Groundwater Flow*, Geophys. Res. v. 71, no. 4.

DUPUIT, J., 1863, *Etudes théoriques et pratiques sur le mouvement des eaux dans les canaux découverts et à travers les terrains perméables*, 2nd ed., Dunot, Paris, 304 pp.

ELIASON, O. L., and GARDNER, W., 1933, *Computing the Effective Diameter of a Well Battery by Means of Darcy's Law*, Agr. Eng., v. 14, pp. 53-54.

ENGELUND, F., 1951, *Mathematical Discussion of Drainage Problems*, Danish Acad. Tech. Sci. Trans. Bull. 3.

ENGELUND, F., 1953, *On the Laminar and Turbulent Flows of Groundwater through Homogeneous Sand*, Danish Acad. Tech. Sci. Trans. Bull. 4.

ERNST, L. F., 1962, *Ground-Water Flow in the Saturated Zone and its Calculation when Horizontal, Parallel Open Conduits are Present* (in Dutch), Centrum voor Landbouwpublikatie en Landbouwdocumentatie, Wageningen.

FAIR, G. M., and HATCH, L. P., 1933, *Fundamental Factors Governing the Streamline Flow of Water through Sand*, J. Am. Water Works Assoc., v. 25, pp. 1551-1565.

FERRIS, J. G., 1950, *A Quantitative Method for Determining Ground-Water Characteristics for Drainage Design*, Agric. Eng., v. 31, pp. 285-289.

FERRIS, J. G., and SAYRE, A. N., 1955, *The Quantitative Approach to Ground-Water Investigations*, Econ. Geology, 50th Anniv. Volume, pp. 714-747.

FERRIS, J. G., 1959, *Ground Water*, in C. O. Wisler and E. F. Brater, *Hydrology*, Chap. 7, John Wiley & Sons, Inc., New York.

FERRIS, J. G. and others, 1962, *Theory of Aquifer Tests*, U. S. Geol. Survey Water Supply Paper 1536-E.

FOLEY, F. C. and others, 1953, *Ground-Water Conditions in the Milwaukee-Waukesha Area, Wisconsin*, U. S. Geol. Survey Water Supply Paper 1229.

FORCHHEIMER, P., 1886, *Über die Ergiebigkeit von Brunnenanlagen und Sickerschlitzen*, Z. Architekt-Ing-Verein, Hannover, v. 32, no. 7.

FREEZE, R. A., and WITHERSPOON, P. A., 1966, *Theoretical Analysis of Regional Groundwater Flow:* 1. *Analytical and Numerical Solutions to the Mathematical Model,* Water Resources Res., v. 2, no. 4, pp. 641-656.

FREEZE, R. A., and WITHERSPOON, P. A., 1966, *Theoretical Analysis of Regional Groundwater Flow:* 2. *Effect of Water-Table Configuration and Subsurface Permeability Variation,* Water Resources Res., v. 3, no. 2, 623-634.

FREEZE, R. A., 1969, *The Mechanism of Natural Ground-Water Recharge and Discharge.* 1. *One-Dimensional, Vertical, Unsteady, Unsaturated Flow above a Recharging or Discharging Ground-Water Flow System,* Water Resources Res., v. 5, no. 1, p. 153.

GARDNER, W. and others, 1928, *The Drainage of Land Overlying Artesian Basins,* Soil Sci., v. 26.

GLOVER, R. E., and BITTINGER, M. W., 1959, *Transient Ground Water Hydraulics,* Colorado State Univ. Pub. CER 59 REG 16, 57 pp.

GLOVER, R. E., 1966, *Ground Water Movement,* Bur. of Reclamation, Eng. Monograph 31, Denver, Colo.

GUYTON, W. F., 1941, *Applications of Coefficients of Transmissibility and Storage to Regional Problems in the Houston District, Texas,* Trans. Am. Geophys. Union, 21st Ann. Meeting, pt. 3.

HAGEN, G., 1839, *Bewegung des Wassers in engen cylindrischen Rohren,* Pogg. Ann. v. 47.

HALL, H. P., 1955, *An Investigation of Steady Flow toward a Gravity Well,* La Houille Blanche, v. 10, pp. 8-35.

HAMEL, G., 1934, *Uber Grundwasserströmung,* Zeitschr. Angew, Math. Mech., v. 14

HANSEN, V. E., 1953, *Unconfined Ground-Water Flow to Multiple Wells,* Trans. Am. Soc. Civil Engrs., v. 118, pp. 1098-1130.

HANSEN, V. E., 1955, *Infiltration and Water Movement during Irrigation,* Soil Sci., v. 79, pp. 93-105.

HANTUSH, M. S., and JACOB, C. E., 1954, *Plane Potential Flow of Ground-waters with Linear Leakage,* Trans. Am. Geophys. Union, v. 35, pp. 917-936.

HANTUSH, M. S., and JACOB, C. E., 1955, *Nonsteady Radial Flow in an Infinite Leaky Aquifer and Nonsteady Green's Functions for an Infinite Strip of Leaky Aquifer,* Trans. Am. Geophys. Union, v. 36, pp. 95-112.

HANTUSH, M. S., and JACOB, C. E., 1955, *Steady Three-Dimensional Flow to a Well in a Two-Layered Aquifer,* Trans. Am. Geophys. Union, v. 36, pp. 286-292.

HANTUSH, M. S., 1957, *Nonsteady Flow to a Well Partially Penetrating an Infinite Leaky Aquifer,* Proc. Iraqi Sci. Soc., v. 1, pp. 10-19.

HANTUSH, M. S., 1959, *Non-Steady Flow to Flowing Wells in Leaky Aquifers,* J. Geophys. Res., v. 64, no. 8.

HANTUSH, M. S., 1960, *Modification of the Theory of Leaky Aquifers,* J. of Geophys. Res., v. 65, pp. 3713-3725.

HANTUSH, M. S., and JACOB, C. E., 1960, *Flow to an Eccentric Well in a Leaky Circular Aquifer,* J. of Geophys. Res., v. 65, pp. 3425-3431.

HANTUSH, M. S., 1961, *Drawdown around a Partially Penetrating Well,* Am. Soc. Civil Engrs., J. of Hydraulics Div., pp. 83-98, July.

HANTUSH, M. S., 1962, *Flow of Groundwater in Sands of Nonuniform Thickness,* J. of Geophys. Res., v. 67, pp. 703-720 and 1527-1535.

HANTUSH, M. S., 1962, *Drainage Wells in Leaky Water-Table Aquifers,* Am. Soc. Civil Engrs. J. Hydraulics Div. pp. 123-137, March.

HANTUSH, M. S., 1964, *Hydraulics of Wells,* in: V. T. Chow (ed.), *Advances in Hydroscience,* v. 1, pp. 281-432, Academic Press, New York.

HANTUSH, M. S., 1966, *A Method for Analyzing a Draw-down Test in Anisotropic Aquifers,* Water Resources Res., v. 2, no. 2, pp. 281-285.

HANTUSH, M. S., 1966, *Wells in Homogeneous Anisotropic Aquifers,* Water Resources Res., v. 2, no. 2, pp. 273-279.

HANTUSH, M. S., 1967, *Flow of Groundwater in Relatively Thick Leaky Aquifers,* Water Resources Res., v. 3, no. 2.

HATCH, L. P., 1940, *Flow Through Granular Media,* J. Appl. Mech., v. 7A, pp. 109-112.

HAUSHILD, W., and KRUSE, G., 1960, *Unsteady Flow of Ground Water into Surface Reservoir,* Proc. Am. Soc. Civil Engrs. no. HY7, pp. 13-20.

HERBERT, ROBIN, 1969, *A Design Method for Deep Well Dewatering Installations,* Ground Water, v. 7, no. 2, pp. 24-34.

HOPF, L., and TREFFTZ, E., 1921, *Grundwasserströmung in einen abfallenden Gelande mit Abfanggraben,* Zeitschr. Angew Math. Mech., v. 1.

HORTON, R. E., 1906, *Surface Drainage of Land by Tile,* Mich. Engr.

HUBBERT, M. K., 1940, *The Theory of Groundwater Motion,* J. Geol., v. 48, no. 8.

HUBBERT, M. K., 1953, *Entrapment of Petroleum under Hydrodynamic Conditions,* Bull. Am. Assoc. Petroleum Geol. v. 37, no. 8.

HUBBERT, M. K., 1956, *Darcy's Law and the Field Equations of the Flow of Underground Fluids,* Trans., Am. Inst. Mining and Metall. Engrs., v. 207, pp. 222-239, also in Bull. Internat. Assoc. Sci. Hydrology, no. 5, 1957 and Oct. 1956 issue of J. Petroleum Tech.

HUBBERT, M. K., 1969, *The Theory of Ground-Water Motion and Related Papers* (reprints of 3 papers with corrections and 1856 paper by Henry Darcy), Hafner Publishing Co., New York and London, 310 pp.

HUNT, B. W., 1970, *Unsteady Seepage toward Narrow Ditch,* J. Hydraulics Div., Am. Soc. Civil Engrs., v. 96, no. HY10, Oct.

HURR, R., 1966, *A new Approach for Estimating Transmissibility from Specific Capacity,* Water Resources Res., v. 2, no. 4, pp. 657-663.

IRMAY, S., 1956, *Extension of Darcy Law to Unsteady Unsaturated Flow through Porous Media,* Internat., Assoc., Sci. Hydrology, Symposia Darcy, Pub. 41, pp. 57-66.

ISRAELSEN, O. W., and MCLAUGHLIN, W. W., 1935, *Drainage of Land Overlying an Artesian Ground-Water Reservoir,* Utah Agr. Exp. Sta. Bull. 259.

JACOB, C. E., 1940, *On the Flow of Water in an Elastic Artesian Aquifer,* Trans. Am. Geophys. Union, 21st Ann. Meeting, pt. 2.

JACOB, C. E., 1941, *Notes on the Elasticity of the Lloyd Sand on Long Island, New York,* Trans. Am. Geophys. Union, v. 22, pp. 783-787.

JACOB, C. E., 1946, *Radial Flow in a Leaky Artesian Aquifer,* Trans. Am. Geophys. Union, v. 27, no. 2.

JACOB, C. E., 1947, *Drawdown Test to Determine Effective Radius of Artesian Well,* Trans. Am. Soc. Civil Engrs., v. 112.

JACOB, C. E., 1950, *Flow of Ground Water,* in *Engineering Hydraulics,* Chap. 5, John Wiley & Sons, Inc., New York.

JACOB, C. E., and LOHMAN, S. W., 1952, *Nonsteady Flow to a Well of a Constant Drawdown in an Extensive Aquifer,* Trans. Am. Geophys. Union, v. 33, no. 4.

JACOB, C. E., 1963, *Determining the Permeability of Water-Table Aquifers,* U. S. Geol. Survey Water Supply Paper 1536-I, pp. 245-271.

JACOB, C. E., 1963, *Recovery Method for Determining the Coefficient of Transmissibility,* U. S. Geol. Survey Water Supply Paper 1536-I.

KASHEF, A. I. and others, 1952, *Numerical Solutions of Steady-state and Transient Flow Problems,* Purdue Univ. Exp. Sta. Bull., v. 36, res. ser. 117.

KASHEF, A. I., 1965, *Exact Free Surface of Gravity Wells,* J. Hydraul. Div. Am. Soc. Civil Engrs., v. 91, no. HY4, pp. 167-184.

KASHEF, A. I., 1969, *Ground-Water Movement toward Artificial Cuts,* Water Resources Res., v. 5, no. 5, p. 1032.

KASHEF, A. I., 1970, *Interference between Gravity Wells – Steady State Flow,* Water Resources Bull. v. 6, no. 4, pp. 617-630; also in Ground Water, v. 8, no. 6, pp. 25-33 (1970).

KAZMANN, R. G., 1946, *Notes on Determining the Effective Distance to a line of Recharge,* Trans. Am. Geophys. Union, v. 27, pp. 854-859.

KING, F. H., 1899, *Principles and Conditions of the Movements of Ground Water,* U. S. Geol. Survey 19th Ann. Rep., pt. 2, pp. 59-294.

KIRKHAM, DON, 1945, *Artificial Drainage of Land, Streamline Experiments, the Artesian Basin-III,* Trans. Am. Geophys. Union, v. 26, no. 3.

KIRKHAM, DON, 1959, *Exact Theory of Flow into a Partially Penetrating Well,* J. Geophys. Res. v. 64, pp. 1317-1327.

KIRKHAM, DON, 1964, *Exact Theory of Shape of the Free Surface about a Well in a Semi-Confined Aquifer,* J. Geophys. Res., v. 69, pp. 2537-2549.

KIRKHAM, DON, 1969, *Ground-Water Seepage Patterns to Wells for Unconfined Flow,* Iowa State Water Resources Res. Inst. Rept. W70-02759.

KOZENY, J., 1933, *Theorie und Berechnung der Brunnen,* Wasserkraft and Wasserwirtschaft, v. 28, pp. 88-92, 101-105, and 113-116.

KRAIJENHOFF VAN DE LEUR, D. A., 1958, *A Study of Nonsteady Groundwater Flow with Special Reference to a Reservoir Coefficient,* Ingenieur, v. 70, pp. 87-94.

KRAIJENHOFF VAN DE LEUR, D. A., 1962, *A Study of Nonsteady Ground-Water Flow, II, Computation Methods for Flow to Drains,* Ingenieur, v. 74, pp. 285-292, Utrecht.

LAWRENCE, F. E., and BRAUNWORTH, P. L., 1906, *Fountain Flow of Water in Vertical Pipe,* Trans. Am. Soc. Civil Engrs., v. 57, p. 264.

LEWIS, M. R., 1932, *Flow of Groundwater as Applied to Drainage Wells,* Trans. Am. Soc. Civil Engrs., v. 96.

LINDQUIST, E., 1933, *On the Flow of Water through Porous Soil,* Repts. to the First Congress of Large Dams, Stockholm.

LUTHIN, J. N., and SCOTT, V. H., 1952, *Numerical Analysis of Flow through Aquifers towards Wells,* Agr. Eng. v. 33, no. 5.

LUTHIN, J. N., and DAY, P. R., 1955, *Lateral Flow above a Sloping Water Table,* Proc. Soil Sci. Soc. Am., v. 18, pp. 406-410.

LUTHIN, J. N. (ed.), 1957, *Drainage of Agricultural Lands,* Am. Soc. Agronomy, Madison, Wis., 620 pp.

MAASLAND, D. E. L., and BITTINGER, M. W., (eds.), 1963, *Flow in Porous Media,* Symp. on Transient Water Hydraulics, Fort Collins, Colorado State Univ., 223 pp.

MEINZER, O. E., 1923 (reprinted 1969), *Outline of Ground-Water Hydrology, with Definitions,* U. S. Geol. Survey Water Supply Paper 494.

MEINZER, O. E., and HARD, H. A., 1925, *The Artesian Water Supply of the Dakota Sandstone in North Dakota, with Special Reference to the Edgeley Quadrangle,* U. S. Geol. Surv. Water Supply Paper 520.

MEINZER, O. E., and FISHEL, V. C., 1934, *Tests of Permeability with Low Hydraulic Gradients,* Trans. Am. Geophys. Union, v. 15.

MELESCHENKO, N. T., 1936, *Analysis of Groundwater Movement under Structures Equipped with Drainage Openings,* Izv. Nauchn. Issled, Inst. Gidrothn, v. 19.

MEYER, R., 1955, *A Few Recent Theoretical Results Concerning Ground-Water Flow,* La Houille Blanche, v. 10, pp. 86-108.

MJATIEV, A. N., 1947, *Pressure Complex of Underground Water and Wells,* Isvestiya Akademiya Nauk, USSR Div. Tech. Sci., no 9.

MOBASHERI, F., and SHAHBAZI, M., 1969, *Steady-State Lateral Movement of Water through the Unsaturated Zone of an Unconfined Aquifer,* Ground Water, v. 7, no. 6, pp. 28-35.

MOGG, J. L., 1959, *The Effect of Aquifer Turbulence on Well Drawdown,* Proc. Am. Soc. Civil Engrs., Hydraulics Div., pp. 99-112, Nov.

MUSKAT, M., 1932, *Potential Distributions in Large Cylindrical Disks with Partially Penetrating Electrodes,* Physics, v. 2.

MUSKAT, M., 1937, *The Flow of Homogeneous Fluids through Porous Media,* McGraw-Hill Book Co., Inc., New York, 737 pp (2nd printing, Edwards Brothers, Ann Arbor, 1946).

MUSKAT, M., 1949, *Physical Principles of Oil Production,* McGraw-Hill Book Co., Inc., New York, 922 pp.

NAHRGANG, G., 1954, *Zur Theorie des volkommen und unvolkommen Brunnens,* J. Springer, Berlin, 43 pp.

NEUMAN, S. P., and WITHERSPOON, P. A., 1969, *Theory of Flow in a Confined Two Aquifer System,* Water Resources Res., v. 5, no. 4, pp. 803-816.

NEUMAN, S. P., and WITHERSPOON, P. A., 1970, *Variational Principles for Confined and Unconfined Flow of Ground Water,* Water Resources Res., v. 6, no. 5, Oct.

PAPADOPULOS, I. S., 1965, *Nonsteady Flow to a Well in an Infinite Anisotropic Aquifer,* Symp. Internat. Assoc. Sci. Hydrology, Dubrovnik.

PAPADOPULOS, I. S. and COOPER, H. H., Jr., 1967, *Drawdown in a Well of Large Diameter,* Water Resources Res., v. 3, no. 1, pp. 241-244.

PETERSON, D. F., Jr., 1955, *Hydraulics of Wells,* Proc. Am. Soc. Civil Engrs. v. 81, sep. 708, 23 pp.

POISEVILLE, J. M., 1846, *Experimental Investigations on the Flow of Liquids in Tubes of Very Small Diameters,* Proc. Roy. Acad. Sci. Inst., France, Math. Phys. Sci. Mem.

REMSON, IRWIN and others, 1959, *Zone of Aeration and its Relationship to Ground-Water Recharge,* J. Am. Water Works Assoc., v. 51, p. 371, Mar.

RIJTEMA, P. E., and WASSINK, H. (eds.), 1968, *Water in the Unsaturated Zone,* Proc. Symp. Wageningen, June 19-25, 1966, Internat. Assoc. Sci. Hydrology, Pub. nos. 82 and 83.

ROSE, H. E., 1945, *An Investigation into the Laws of Flow of Fluids through Beds of Granular Materials,* Proc. Inst. Mech. Engrs., v. 153, pp. 141-148.

ROSE, H. E., 1945, *On the Resistance Coefficient-Reynolds Number Relationship for Fluid Flow through a Bed of Granular Material,* Proc. Inst. Mech. Engrs. v. 153, pp. 154-168.

RUSSELL, W. L., 1928, *The Origin of Artesian Pressure,* Econ. Geol., v. 23, pp. 132-157.

SAYRE, A. N., 1950, *Ground Water,* Sci. Am., v. 183, no. 5, pp. 14-19.

SCHEIDEGGER, A. E., 1957, *On the Theory of Flow of Miscible Phases in Porous Media,* Internat. Assoc. Sci. Hydrology, General Assembly Toronto, Pub. 44, v. 2, pp. 236-242.

SCHNEEBELI, G., 1955, *Experiences sur la limite de validité de la loi de Darcy et l'apparition de la turbulence dans un écoulement de filtration,* La Houille Blanche, v. 10, no. 2, pp. 141-149.

SHAW, F. S., and SOUTHWELL, R. V., 1941, *Relaxation Methods Applied to Engineering Problems, Pt. VII, Problems Relating to the Percolation of Fluids through Porous Materials,* Proc. Roy. Soc. London, ser. A, v. 178.

SLICHTER, C. S., 1898, *Theoretical Investigations of the Motion of Groundwaters,* U. S. Geol. Surv. 19th Ann. Rept. pt. 2.

SLICHTER, C. S., 1902, *The Motion of Underground Waters,* U. S. Geol. Survey Water Supply Paper 67.

SLICHTER, C. S., 1905, *Field Measurements of the Rate of Movement of Underground Water,* U. S. Geol. Survey Water Supply Paper 140.

SMITH, W. O., 1961, *Mechanism of Gravity Drainage and its Relation to Specific Yield of Uniform Sands,* U. S. Geol. Survey Prof. Paper 402-A 1961.

SMITH, W. O., 1967, *Infiltration in Sands and its Relation to Groundwater Recharge,* Water Resources Res., v. 3, no. 2.

STALLMAN, R. W., and PAPADOPULOS, I. S., 1966, *Measurement of Hydraulic Diffusivity of Wedge-Shaped Aquifers Drained by Streams,* U. S. Geol. Survey Prof. Paper 514, 50 pp.

STEGGEWENTZ, J. H., and VAN NES, B. A., 1939, *Calculating the Yield of a Well Taking Account of Replenishment of the Groundwater from Above,* Water and Water Eng. v. 41, pp. 561-563.

STERNBERG, Y. M., 1969, *Flow to Wells in the Presence of Radial Discontinuities,* Ground Water, v. 7, no. 6, pp. 17-21.

SWARTZENDRUBER, D., 1962, *Non-Darcy Flow Behaviour in Liquid Saturated Porous Media,* J. Geophys. Res., v. 67, Dec., pp. 5205-5213.

TAYLOR, G. S., and LUTHIN, J. N., 1969, *Computer Methods for Transient Analysis of Water-Table Aquifers,* Water Resources Res., v. 5, no. 1, p. 144.

THEIS, C. V., 1932, *Equations for Lines of Flow in Vicinity of Discharging Artesian Well,* Trans. Am. Geophys. Union, v. 13, pp. 317-320.

THEIS, C. V., 1935, *The Relation between the Lowering of the Piezometric Surface and the Rate and Duration of Discharge of a Well Using Groundwater Storage,* Trans. Am. Geophys. Union, v. 16, pp. 519-524.

THEIS, C. V., 1937, *Amount of Ground-Water Recharge in the Southern High Plains,* Trans. Am. Geophys. Union, 18th Ann. Meeting, pt. 2.

THEIS, C. V., 1938, *The Significance and Nature of the Cone of Depression in Ground-Water Bodies,* Econ. Geol., v. 33, pp. 889-902.

THIEM, A., 1870, *Die Ergiebigkeit artesischer Bohrlocher, Schachtbrunnen und Filter-gallerien,* J. Gasbeleuchtung Wasserversorgung, v. 14, Munich.

THIEM, G., 1906, *Hydrologische Methoden,* J. M. Gephardt, Leipzig.

VAN VOAST, W. A., and NOVITZKI, R. P., 1966, *Ground Water Flow Related to Streamflow and Water Quality,* Water Resources Res., v. 4, no. 4, Aug.

VERDERNIKOV, V. V., 1934, *Versickerung aus Kanalen,* Wasserkraft Wasserwirtsch., vs. 11-13.

VREEDENBURGH, C. G. J., and STEVENS, O. M., 1936, *Electric Investigation of Underground Water Flow Nets,* Proc. Internat. Conf. Soil Mech. Found. Eng., v. 1.

WALTON, W. C., 1955, *Ground-water Hydraulics as an Aid to Geologic Interpretation,* Ohio, J. Sci., v. 55, no. 1.

WARD, J. C., 1964, *Turbulent Flow in Porous Media,* J. Hydraulics Div., Am. Soc. Civil Engrs., Sept., pp. 1-12.

WENZEL, L. K., 1933, *Specific Yield Determined from a Thiem's Pumping Test,* Trans. Am. Geophys. Union, v. 14, pp. 475-477.

WENZEL, L. K., 1936, *The Thiem Method for Determining Permeability of Water-Bearing Materials and its Application to the Determination of Specified Yield, Results of Investigations in the Platte River Valley, Nebr.,* U. S. Geol. Surv. Water Supply Paper 679-A.

WENZEL, L. K., 1942, *Methods for Determining Permeability of Water-Bearing Materials with Special Reference to Discharging-Well Methods,* U. S. Geol. Survey Water Supply Paper 887, 192 pp.

WENZEL, L. K., and SAND. H. H., 1942, *Water Supply of the Dakota Sandstone in the Ellentown-Jamestown Area, North Dakota,* U. S. Geol. Surv. Water Supply Paper 889-A.

WENZEL, L. K., and GREENLEE, A. L., 1943, *A Method for Determining Transmissibility and Storage Coefficients by Tests of Multiple Well Systems,* Trans. Am. Geophys. Union, v. 24, pp. 547-564.

WERNER, P. W., 1957, *Some Problems in Non-Artesian Groundwater Flow,* Trans. Am. Geophys. Union, v. 38, pp. 511-518.

WIGLEY, T. M. L., 1968, *Flow into a Finite Well with Arbitrary Discharge,* J. Hydrology, v. 6, no. 2, Apr.

WOLF, R. G., 1970, *Field and Laboratory Determination of the Hydraulic Diffusivity of a Confining Bed,* Water Resources Res., v. 6, no. 1, p. 194, Feb.

WOODING, R. A., and CHAPMAN, T. G., 1966, *Groundwater Flow over a Sloping Impermeable Layer,* J. Geophys. Res., v. 71, no. 12.

WYLLIE, M. R. J., and SPANGLER, M. B., 1952, *Application of Electrical Resistivity Measurements to Problem of Fluid Flow in Porous Media,* Bull. Am. Assoc. Petroleum Geologists, v. 36, pp. 359-403.

YANG, S. T., 1949, *Seepage toward a Well Analyzed by the Relaxation Method,* Doctoral Thesis, Harvard Univ.

YOUNGS, E. G., 1969, *Unconfined Aquifers and the Concept of the Specific Yield,* Bull. Internat. Assoc. Sci. Hydrology, v. 14, no. 2, June.

ZANGAR, C. N., 1953, *Flow in Porous Media* — Theory and Problems of Water Percolation, U. S. Bur. Reclam., Eng. Monograph 8, Denver, 76 pp.

PUMPING TESTS AND FIELD OBSERVATIONS

BENNETT, G. D., and PATTEN, E. P., Jr., 1962, *Constant-Head Pumping Test of a Multiaquifer Well to Determine Characteristics of Individual Aquifers,* U. S. Geol. Survey Water Supply Paper 1536-G, pp. 181-203.

BENTALL, RAY, 1963, *Methods of Determining Permeability, Transmissibility and Drawdown,* U. S. Geol. Survey Water Supply Paper 1536-I, pp. 243-341.

BENTALL, RAY (compiler), 1963, *Shortcuts and Special Problems in Aquifer Tests,* U. S. Geol. Survey Water Supply Paper 1545-C, 117 pp.

BIANCHI, W. C., and HASKELL, E. E., Jr., 1968, *Field Observations Compared with Dupuit-Forchheimer Theory for Mound Heights under a Recharge Basin,* Water Resources Res., v. 4, no. 5, pp. 1049-1059.

BIERSCHENK, W. H., 1964, *Determining Well Efficiency by Multiple Step-Drawdown Tests,* Internat. Assoc. Sci. Hydrology, Pub. 64.

BOULTON, N. S., 1963, *Analysis of Data from Non-Equilibrium Pumping Tests Allowing for Delayed Yield from Storage,* Proc. Inst. Civil Engrs., London, v. 26, no. 6693.

BOULTON, N. S., 1964, *Discussions on the Analysis of Data from Nonequilibrium Pumping Tests Allowing for Delayed Yield from Storage,* Proc. Inst. Civil Engrs., v. 28, London.

BOULTON, N. S., 1970, *Analysis of Data from Pumping Tests in Unconfined Anisotropic Aquifers,* J. Hydrology, v. 10, no. 4, June.

BROWN, R. H., 1953, *Selected Procedures for Analyzing Aquifer Test Data,* J. Am. Water Works Assoc., v. 45, no. 8, pp. 844-866, New York.

BRUIN, J., and HUDSON, H. E., Jr., 1955, *Selected Methods for Pumping Test Analyses,* Illinois State Water Surv. Rept. of Invest. 25.

CALIFORNIA DEPT. OF WATER RESOURCES, 1963, *Permeability, Coefficients of Transmissibility, Coefficients of Storage, Methods of Determination and Application to Ground-Water Problems – Annotated Bibliography through 1961,* 75 pp.

44

CHOW, V. T., 1951, *Drawdown in Artesian Wells Computed by Nomograph,* Civil Eng., v. 21, no. 10, pp. 48-49.

CHOW, V. T., 1952, *On the Determination of Transmissibility and Storage Coefficients from Pumping Test Data,* Trans. Am. Geophys. Union, v. 33, pp. 397-404.

COOPER, H. H., Jr., and JACOB, C. E., 1946, *A Generalized Graphical Method for Evaluating Formation Constants and Summarizing Well-Field History,* Trans. Am. Geophys. Union, v. 27, pp. 526-534.

FERRIS, J. G., 1948, *Groundwater Hydraulics as a Geophysical Aid,* Mich. Dept. Conserv., Geol. Surv. Div. Tech. Rept. 1.

FOOSE, R. M., 1969, *Mine Dewatering and Recharge in Carbonate Rocks near Hershey, Pennsylvania,* in *Legal Aspects of Geology in Engineering Practice,* Geol. Soc. Am. Eng. Case Histories, no. 7, pp. 45-60.

GARBER, M. S., and KOOPMAN, F. C., 1968, *Methods of Measuring Water Levels in Deep Wells,* U. S. Geol. Survey Techniques of Water Resources Inv. Book 8, Chapter A-1, 23 pp.

GERAGHTY, J. J. and others, 1967, *The Status of Ground-Water Resources of Nansemond County and Isle of Wight County, Virginia,* Geraghty & Miller, Inc., Port Washington, N. Y., 61 pp.

GILLILAND, J. A., 1968, *Digitizing, Storing and Recovering Observations-Well Hydrographs,* J. Hydrology, v. 6, no. 2, Apr.

GUYTON, W. F., 1942, *Results of Pumping Tests of the Carrizo Sand in the Lufkin Area, Texas,* Trans. Am. Geophys. Union, v. 22, pt. 1, pp. 40-48.

HANTUSH, M. S., 1956, *Analysis of Data from Pumping Tests in Leaky Aquifers,* Trans. Am. Geophys. Union, v. 37, pp. 702-714.

HANTUSH, M. S., 1961, *Economical Spacing of Interfering Wells,* Internat. Assoc. Sci. Hydrology, Publ. no. 57, pp. 350-364.

HANTUSH, M. S., 1964, *Depletion of Storage, Leakage, and River Flow by Gravity Wells in Sloping Sands,* J. of Geophys. Res., v. 69, pp. 2551-60.

HARRILL, J. R., 1970, *Determining Transmissivity from Water-Level Recovery of a Step-Drawdown Test,* U. S. Geol. Survey Prof. Paper 700-C, pp. 212-213.

HIRD, J. M., 1969, *Control of Artesian Ground Water in Strip Mining Phosphate Ores in Eastern North Carolina* (abs), Mining Eng., v. 21, no. 12, p. 55.

INESON, J., 1963, *Applications and Limitations of Pumping Tests, Hydrogeological Significance,* J. Inst. Water Engrs., v. 17, pp. 200-215.

JACOB, C. E., 1944, *Notes on Determining Permeability by Pumping Tests under Water-Table Conditions,* U. S. Geol. Survey mimeographed report.

JACOB, C. E., 1946, *Drawdown Test to Determine Effective Radius of Artesian Well,* Proc. Am. Soc. Civil Engrs., v. 79, no. 5.

JOHNSON, C. R., and GREENKORN, R. A., 1960, *Comparison of Core Analysis and Drawdown Test Results from a Water-Bearing Upper Pennsylvanian Sandstone of Central Oklahoma,* Bull. Geol. Soc. America, v. 71, pp. 1898.

KANO, T., 1939, *Frictional Loss of Head in the Wall of a Well,* Japan J. Astron. Geophys., v. 17, no. 1.

KRUSEMAN, G. P., and DE RIDDER, N. A., 1970, *Analysis and Evaluation of Pumping Test Data,* Internat. Inst. for Land Reclamation and Improvement, Bull. 11, Wageningen, The Netherlands.

LANG, S. M., 1960, *Interpretation of Boundary Effects from Pumping Test Data,* J. Am. Water Works Assoc., v. 52, no. 3, pp. 356-364.

LANG, S. M., 1963, *Drawdown Patterns in Aquifers Having a Straight-Line Boundary,* U. S. Geol. Survey Water Supply Paper 1545-C.

LEE, C. H., 1934, *The Interpretation of Water-Levels in Wells and Test-Holes,* Trans. Am. Geophys. Union, v. 15, pp. 540-554.

LENNOX, D. H., 1966, *The Analysis and Application of the Step-Drawdown Test,* J. Hydraulics Div., Am. Soc. Civil Engrs., v. 92, no. HY 6, Proc. Paper no. 4967.

LENNOX, D. H., and VANDENBERG, ALBERT, 1967, *Drawdowns due to Cyclic Pumping,* J. Hydraulics Div. Proc. Am. Soc. Civil Engrs., v. 93, no. HY6, Nov.

LI, W. H., 1954, *Interaction between Well and Aquifer,* Proc. Am. Soc. Civil Engrs., v. 80, sep. 578, 14 pp.

LOGAN, J., 1964, *Estimating Transmissibility from Routine Production Tests of Water Wells,* Ground Water, v. 2, no. 2, pp. 35-37.

MOGG, J. L., 1969, *Step-Drawdown Test Needs Critical Review,* Ground Water, v. 7, no. 1.

PARIZEK, R. R., and SIDDIQUI, S. H., 1970, *Determining the Sustained Yields of Wells in Carbonate and Fractured Aquifers,* Ground Water, v. 8, no. 5, pp. 12-21.

PATCHICK, P. F., 1967, *Estimating Water Well Specific Capacity Utilizing Permeability of Disturbed Samples,* J. Am. Water Works Assoc., v. 59, p. 1292, Oct.

PETERSEN, J. S. and others, 1955, *Effect of Well Screens on Flow into Wells,* Trans. Am. Soc. Civil Engrs., v. 120, pp. 563-607.

PRICKETT, T. A., 1965, *Type-Curve Solution to Aquifer Tests under Water-Table Conditions,* Ground Water, v. 3, no. 3.

REMSON, I., and LANG, S. M., 1955, *A Pumping-Test Method for the Determination of Specific Yield,* Trans. Am. Geophys. Union, v. 36, pp. 321-325.

REMSON, I., and VAN HYLCKEMA, T. E. A., 1956, *Nomographs for the Rapid Analysis of Aquifer Tests,* J. Am. Water Works Assoc., v. 48, pp. 511-516.

RORABAUGII, M. I., 1953, *Graphical and Theoretical Analysis of Step Drawdown Test of Artesian Well,* Proc. Am. Soc. Civil Engrs., v. 79.

SHUTER, E., and JOHNSON, A. I., 1961, *Evaluation of Equipment for Measurement of Water Level in Wells of Small Diameter,* U. S. Geol. Survey Cir. 453, 12 pp.

SLICHTER, C. S., 1904, *Approximate Methods of Measuring the Yield of Flowing Wells,* U. S. Geol. Survey Water Supply Paper 110, pp. 37-42.

STERNBERG, Y. M., 1968, *Simplified Solution for Variable Rate Pumping Test,* J. Hydraulics Div. Am. Soc. Civil Engrs., v. 94, no. HY1, Jan.

STEWART, D. M., 1970, *The Rock and Bong Techniques of Measuring Water Levels in Wells,* Ground Water, v. 8, no. 6, pp. 14-19.

THEIS, C. V., 1963, *Drawdowns Caused by a Well Discharging under Equilibrium Conditions from an Aquifer, Bounded on a Finite Straight-Line Source,* in *Shortcuts and Special Problems in Aquifer Tests,* U. S. Geol. Survey Water Supply Paper 1545-C.

TURCAN, A. N., Jr., 1963, *Estimating the Specific Capacity of a Well,* U. S. Geol. Surv. Prof. Paper 450-E.

VAN POOLLEN, H. K., 1961, *Status of Drill-Stem Testing Techniques and Analysis,* J. Petroleum Tech., pp. 333-339, Apr.

WALTON, W. C., 1960, *Leaky Artesian Aquifer Conditions in Illinois,* Illinois State Water Survey Rept. of Invest. 39.

WALTON, W. C., and STEWART, J. W., 1961, *Aquifer Tests in the Snake River Basalt,* Trans. Am. Soc. Civil Engnrs., v. 126, pp. 612-632.

WALTON, W. C., 1962, *Selected Analytical Methods for Well and Aquifer Evaluation,* Illinois State Water Survey Bull. 49.

WALTON, W. C., and NEILL, J. C., 1963, *Statistical Analysis of Specific Capacity Data for a Dolomite Aquifer,* J. Geophys. Res., v. 68, pp. 2251-2262.

WENZEL, L. K., and GREENLEE, A. L., 1943, *A Method for Determining Transmissibility and Storage Coefficients by Tests of Multiple Well-Systems,* Trans. Am. Geophys. Union, 24th Ann. Meeting, pt. 2.

TRACERS

AMBROSE, A. W., 1921, *Use of Detectors for Tracing Movement of Underground Water,* U. S. Bureau Mines Bull. 195, Washington, D. C., pp. 106-120.

BAETSLE, L. H., and SOUFFRIA, J., 1966, *Fundamentals of the Dispersion of Radionuclides in Sandy Aquifers,* Isotopes in Hydrology, Symp. Vienna, Internat. Atomic Energy Agency, pp. 617-628.

CARLSTON, C. W. and others, 1960, *Tritium as a Hydrologic Tool, the Wharton Tract Study,* Internat. Assoc. Sci. Hydrol. Pub. no. 52, pp. 503-512.

CARTER, R. C. and others, 1959, *Helium as a Ground-Water Tracer,* J. Geophys. Res., v. 64, pp. 2433-2439.

DANEL, P., 1953, *The Measurement of Ground-Water Flow,* Proc. Ankara Symp. on Arid Zone Hydrology, pp. 99-107, UNESCO, Paris.

DE LAGUNA, WALLACE, 1970, *Tracer Aids Interpretation of Pumping Test,* Water Resources Res., v. 6, no. 1, p. 172, Feb.

DOLE, R. B., 1906, *Use of Fluorescein in the Study of Underground Water,* U. S. Geol. Survey Water Supply Paper 160, pp. 73-86.

FOX, C. S., 1952, *Using Radioactive Isotopes to Trace Movement of Underground Waters,* Municipal Utilities, v. 90, no. 4, pp. 30-32.

HALEVY, E., and NIR, A., 1962, *The Determination of Aquifer Parameters with the Aid of Radioactive Tracers*, J. Geophys. Res., v. 67, no. 6.

HARPAZ, Y. and others, 1963, *The Place of Isotope Methods in Ground Water Research*, Radioisotopes in Hydrology, Symp. Tokyo, Internat. Atomic Energy Agency, pp. 175-191.

HOURS, R., 1955, *Radioactive Tracers in Hydrology*, La Houille Blanche, v. 10, no. A, pp. 14-24.

INTERNATIONAL ATOMIC ENERGY AGENCY, 1963, *Radioisotopes in Hydrology*, 449 pp., Vienna, Proc. Symp. on the Application of Radioisotopes in Hydrology, Tokyo, March 5-9, 1963.

KAUFMAN, W. J., and TODD, D. K., 1955, *Methods of Detecting and Tracing the Movement of Ground Water*, Inst. Eng. Research Rep. 93-1, Univ. of California, Berkeley, 130 pp.

KAUFMAN, W. J., and ORLOB, G. T., 1956, *Measuring Ground Water Movement with Radioactive and Chemical Tracers*, J. Am. Water Works Assoc., v. 48, pp. 559-572.

KAUFMAN, W. J., and ORLOB, G. T., 1956, *An Evaluation of Ground-Water Tracers*, Trans. Am. Geophys. Union, v. 37, pp. 297-306.

KAUFMAN, W. J., 1960, *The Use of Radioactive Tracers in Hydrologic Studies*, Univ. of California, Proc. Conference on Water Res., Water Resources Center Rept. 2, pp. 6-14.

KAUFMAN, W. J., 1961, *Tritium as a Ground Water Tracer*, Trans. Am. Soc. Civil. Engnrs. Paper 3203, pp. 436-446.

KEYS, N. S., 1966, *The Application of Radiation Logs to Groundwater Hydrology*, Isotopes in Hydrology, Symp. Vienna, Internat. Atomic Energy Agency, SM 83/33, pp. 477-486.

MATHER, J. D., 1968, *A Literature Survey of the Use of Radioisotopes in Ground-Water Studies*, Great Britain Inst. of Geol. Sciences, Tech. Communication no. 1, London.

NELSON, R. W., and REISENAUER, A. E., 1963, *Application of Radioactive Tracers in Scientific Ground Water Hydrology*, Radioisotopes in Hydrology, Symp. Tokyo, Internat. Atomic Energy Agency, pp. 207-230.

RIFAI, M. N. E. and others, 1956, *Dispersion Phenomena in Laminar Flow through Porous Media*, Inst. Eng. Res. Rep. 93-2, Univ. Calif. Berkeley, 157 pp.

SCHOFF, S. L., and MOORE, J. E., 1968, *Sodium as a Clue to Direction of Ground-Water Movement, Nevada Test Site,* U. S. Geol. Survey Prof. Paper 600-D, pp. 30-33.

SUGISAKI, R., 1961, *Measurement of Effective Flow Velocity of Ground Water by Means of Dissolved Gases,* Am. Jour. Sci., v. 259, pp. 144-153.

THEIS, C. V., 1963, *Hydrologic Phenomena Affecting the Use of Tracers in Timing GroundWater Flow,* Radioisotopes in Hydrology, Symp. Tokyo, Internat. Atomic Energy Agency, pp. 193-206.

VON BUTTLAR, H., and WENDT, I., 1958, *Ground-Water Studies in New Mexico Using Tritium as a Tracer,* Trans. Am. Geophys. Union, v. 39, pp. 660-668.

VON BUTTLAR, H., 1959, *Ground-Water Studies in New Mexico Using Tritium as a Tracer, Part II,* J. Geophys. Res., v. 64, pp. 1031-1038.

WIEBENGA, W. A. and others, 1967, *Radioisotopes as Groundwater Tracers,* J. Geophys. Res., v. 72, no. 15.

CHEMICAL QUALITY AND WATER STANDARDS

AMERICAN PUBLIC HEALTH ASSOCIATION, AMERICAN WATER WORKS ASSOCIATION and WATER POLLUTION CONTROL FEDERATION, 1965, *Standard Methods for the Examination of Water, Sewage and Industrial Wastes,* 12th ed., Water Pollution Control Fed., Washington, D. C.

AMERICAN SOCIETY FOR TESTING MATERIALS, 1970, *Water and Atmospheric Analysis,* Philadelphia, Pa., 1,072 pp.

ANONYMOUS, 1940, *Progress Report of the Committee on Quality Tolerances of Water for Industrial Uses,* J. New Engl. Water Works Assoc., v. 54.

BACK, WILLIAM, 1960, *Origin of Hydrochemical Facies of Ground Water in the Atlantic Coastal Plain,* Internat. Geol. Cong., 21 Session, Part 1, Geochemical Cycles, pp. 87-95.

BACK, WILLIAM, 1961, *Techniques for Mapping Hydrochemical Facies,* U. S. Geol. Surv. Prof. Paper 424-D.

BACK, WILLIAM, 1963, *Preliminary Results of a Study of Calcium Carbonate Saturation of Ground Water in Central Florida,* Internat. Assoc. Sci. Hydrology, 8th year, no. 3, pp. 43-51.

BACK, WILLIAM, 1966, *Hydrochemical Facies and Ground-Water Flow Patters in Northern Part of Atlantic Coastal Plain,* U. S. Geol. Survey Prof. Paper 498-A.

BAKER, R. C. and others, 1964, *Natural Sources of Salinity in the Brazos River, Texas-with Particular Reference to the Croton and Salt Croton Creek Basins,* U. S. Geol. Survey Water Supply Paper 1669-CC, 81 pp.

BARNES, IVAN, and CLARKE, F. E., 1964, *Geochemistry of Ground Water in Mine Drainage Problems,* U. S. Geol. Survey Prof. Paper 473-A, 6 pp.

BODVARSSON, GUNNAR, 1969, *On the Temperature of Water Flowing through Fractures,* J. Geophys. Res., v. 74, no. 8, Apr.

BÜHLER, U. G. and others, 1968, *On the Treatment of a Ground Water Containing High Percentages of Iron and Manganese,* Wasserwirtschaft-Wassertechnik, v. 18, no. 4.

BRASHEARS, M. L., Jr., 1941, *Ground-Water Temperature on Long Island, New York,* as *Affected by Recharge of Warm Water,* Econ. Geol., v. 36, pp. 811-828.

BREDEHOEFT, J. D. and others, 1963, *Possible Mechanism for Concentration of Brines in Subsurface Formations,* Bull. Am. Assoc. Petroleum Geologists, v. 47, pp. 257-269.

CASE, L. C. and others, 1942, *Selected Annotated Bibliography on Oil Field Waters,* Bull. Am. Assoc. Petroleum Geologists, v. 26, no. 5, p. 865-881.

CLARKE, F. W., 1924, *The Data of Geochemistry,* U. S. Geol. Survey Bull. no. 770, 841 pp.

COLLINS, W. D., 1923, *Graphical Representation of Water Analyses,* Ind. Eng. Chem., v. 15.

COLLINS, W. D., 1925, *Temperature of Water Available for Industrial Use in the United States,* U. S. Geol. Survey Water Supply Paper 520-F.

DE GEOFFROY, J. G. and others, 1967, *Geochemical Coverage by Spring Sampling Method in Southwest Wisconsin,* Econ. Geol., v. 62, pp. 679-697.

DONEEN, L. D., 1954, *Salination of Soil by Salts in the Irrigation Water,* Trans. Am. Geophys. Union, v. 35, pp. 943-950.

DUROV, S. A., 1948, *Classification of Natural Waters and Graphic Representation of their Composition,* Akad. Nauk., SSSR, v. 59, pp. 87-90.

EATON, F. M., 1935, *Boron in Soils and Irrigation Waters and its Effect on Plants, with Particular Reference to the San Joaquin Valley of California,* U. S. Dept. Agric. Tech. Bull. 448, 131 pp.

FETH, J. H., 1965, *Selected References on Saline Ground Water Resources of the United States,* U. S. Geol. Survey Circ. 499, 30 pp.

FEULNER, A. J., and SCHUPP, R. G., 1963, *Seasonal changes in the Chemical Quality of Shallow Ground Water in Northwestern Alaska,* U. S. Geol. Survey Prof. Paper 475 B, pp. 189-191.

FINK, J. F., 1964, *Groundwater Temperatures in a Tropical Island Environment,* J. of Geophys. Res., v. 69, no. 24.

FIREMAN, M., and MAGISTAD, O. C., 1945, *Permeability of Five Western Soils as Affected by the Percentage of Sodium of the Irrigation Water,* Trans. Am. Geophys. Union, v. 26, pp. 91-94.

FOSTER, M. D., 1942, *Base Exchange and Sulfate Reduction in Salty Ground Waters along Atlantic and Gulf Coasts,* Bull. Am. Assoc. Petroleum Geologists, v. 26, pp. 838-851.

FOSTER, M. D., 1950, *The Origin of High Sodium Bicarbonate Waters in the Atlantic and Gulf Coastal Plains,* Geochim. et Cosmochim. Acta, v. 1, pp. 33-48.

GEORGE, W. O., and HASTINGS, W. W., 1951, *Nitrate in the Ground Water of Texas,* Trans. Am. Geophys. Union, v. 32, pp. 450-456.

GINTER, R. L., 1934, *Sulphate Reduction in Deep Subsurface Waters,* in W. E. Wrather and F. H. Lahee (eds.), *Problems of Petroleum Geology,* Am. Assoc. Petroleum Geologists, Tulsa, Oklahoma, pp. 907-925.

GORHAM, E., 1955, *On the Acidity and Salinity of Rain,* Geochim. et Cosmochim. Acta, v. VII, pp. 231-239.

GORRELL, H. A., 1958, *Classification of Formation Waters based on Sodium Chloride Content,* Bull. Am. Assoc. Petroleum Geologists, v. 42, pp. 2513.

HARDER, A. H., and HOLDEN, W. R., 1965, *Measurement of Gas in Groundwater,* Water Resources Res., v. 1, no. 1, pp. 75-82.

HEATH, R. C., 1964, *Seasonal Temperature Fluctuations in Surficial Sand near Albany, N. Y.,* U. S. Geol. Survey Prof. Paper 475-D, Art. 168, pp. D204-D208.

HEM, J. D., 1950, *Geochemistry of Ground Water,* Econ. Geol. v. 45, pp. 72-81.

HEM, J. D., and CROPPER, W. H., 1959, *Survey of Ferrous-Ferric Chemical Equilibria and Redox Potentials,* U. S. Geol. Survey Water Supply Paper 1459-A, 31 pp.

HEM, J. D., 1961, *Calculation and Use of Ion Activity,* U. S. Geol. Survey Water Supply Paper 1535-C, 17 pp.

HEM, J. D. and others, 1962, *Chemistry of Iron in Natural Water,* U. S. Geol. Survey Water Supply Paper 1459, 269 pp.

HEM, J. D., 1963, *Some Aspects of Chemical Equilibrium in Ground Water,* Ground Water, v. 1, pp. 30-34.

HEM, J. D., 1970, *Study and Interpretation of the Chemical Characteristics of Natural Water,* U. S. Geol. Survey Water Supply Paper 1473, 363 pp.

HILL, R. A., 1942, *Salts in Irrigation Water,* Trans. Am. Soc. Civil Engrs. v. 107.

HISS, W. I., 1970, *Acquisition and Machine Processing of Saline Water Data from Southeastern New Mexico and Western Texas,* J. Water Resources Res., v. 6, no. 5, pp. 1471-1477, Oct.

HUBERTY, M. R., 1941, *Chemical Composition of Ground Waters,* Civil Eng., v. 11, pp. 494-495.

JONES, B. F., 1966, *Geochemical Evolution of Closed Basin Water in the Western Great Basin,* Northern Ohio Geol. Soc., Symp. on Salt, 2nd Proc. v. 1, pp. 181-199.

JUNGE, C. E., and GUSTAFSON, P. E., 1957, *On the Distribution of Sea Salt over the United States and its Removal by Precipitation,* Tellas, v. 9, pp. 164-173.

KELLEY, W. P., 1941, *Permissible Composition and Concentration of Irrigation Water,* Trans. Am. Soc. Civil Engrs. v. 106, pp. 849-861.

LANGELIER, W. F., and LUDWIG, H. F., 1942, *Graphical Methods for Indicating the Mineral Character of Natural Waters,* J. Am. Water Works Assoc., v. 34.

LARSON, T. E., 1949, *Geologic Correlation and Hydrologic Interpretation of Water Analyses,* Water Sewage Works, v. 96, pp. 67-74.

LARSON, T. E., and HENLEY, L. M., 1966, *Occurrence of Nitrate in Well Waters,* Univ. of Illinois Water Resources Center, Res. Rept. no. 1.

LEGRAND, H. E., 1958, *Chemical Character of Water in the Igneous and Metamorphic Rocks of North Carolina,* Econ. Geol., v. 53, pp. 178-189.

LOGAN, J., 1961, *Estimation of Electrical Conductivity from Chemical Analyses of Natural Waters,* J. of Geophys. Res., v. 66, no. 8.

LOVE, S. K., 1944, *Cation Exchange in Groundwater Contaminated with Seawater near Miami, Florida,* Trans. Am. Geophys. Union, 25th ann. meeting, pt. 6.

LOVERING, T. S., and GOODE, H. D., 1963, *Measuring Geothermal Gradients in Drill Holes less than 60 feet deep, East Tintic District, Utah,* U. S. Geol. Survey Bull. 1172.

McKEE, J. E., and WOLF, H. W., (eds.), 1963, *Water Quality Criteria,* Calif. State Water Quality Control Bd., Pub. no. 3-A.

MORGAN, C. O. and others, 1966, *Digital Computer Methods for Water Quality Data,* Ground Water, v. 4, no. 3.

MORGAN, C. O., and McNELLIS, J. M., 1969, *Stiff Diagrams of Water-Quality Data Programmed for the Digital Computer,* Kansas State Geol. Survey Spec. Distrib. Pub. 43.

MORSE, R. R., 1943, *The Nature and Significance of Certain Variations in Composition of Los Angeles Basin Ground Waters,* Econ. Geol., v. 38, pp. 475-511.

MUSSER, J. J., and WHETSTONE, G. W., 1964, *Geochemistry of Water,* in *Influences of Strip Mining in Beaver Creek Basin, Kentucky,* U. S. Geol. Survey Prof. Paper 427-B, pp. B25-48.

OSWALD, W. J., 1967, *Remote Sensing Data and Evaluation of Water Quality,* Proc. Third Ann. Conf. on Remote Sensing of Air and Water Pollution, North Am. Aviation, Inc., Autonetics Div., Anaheim, Calif., pp. 15-1 to 15-12.

PALMER, C., 1911, *The Geochemical Interpretation of Water Analyses,* U. S. Geol. Survey Bull. 479, 31 pp.

PIPER, A. M., 1944, *A Graphic Procedure in the Geochemical Interpretation of Water Analyses,* Trans. Am. Geophys. Union, 25th ann. meeting, pt. 6, Discussion by R. A. Hill, W. F. Langelier, and A. M. Piper.

PIPER, A. M., 1953, *A Graphic Procedure in the Geochemical Interpretation of Water Analyses,* U. S. Geol. Survey Ground Water Note 12.

PIPER, A. M. and others, 1953, *Native and Contaminated Waters in the Long Beach-Santa Ana Area, California,* U. S. Geol. Survey Water Supply Paper 1136, 320 pp.

PLUHOWSKI, E. J., and KANTROWITZ, I. H., 1963, *Influence of Land-Surface Conditions on Ground-Water Temperatures in Southwestern Suffolk County, Long Island, N. Y.,* U. S. Geol. Survey Prof. Paper 475-B, Art. 51, pp. B186-B188.

POWELL, S. T., 1948, *Some Aspects of the Requirements for the Quality of Water for Industrial Purposes,* J. Am. Water Works Assoc., v. 40, pp. 8-23.

PRYOR, W. A., 1956, *Quality of Water Estimated from Electric Resistivity Logs,* Illinois State Geol. Survey Circ. 215.

RAINWATER, F. H., and THATCHER, L. L., 1960, *Methods for Collection and Analysis of Water Samples,* U. S. Geol. Survey Water Supply Paper 1454, 301 pp.

RENICK, B. C., 1925, *Base Exchange in Ground Water by Silicates as Illustrated in Montana,* U. S. Geol. Survey Water Supply Paper 520-D, pp. 53-72.

REVELLE, ROGER, 1941, *Criteria for Recognition of Sea Water in Ground Water,* Trans. Am. Geophys. Union, v. 22, pp. 593-597.

RICHARDS, L. A., (ed.), 1954, *Diagnosis and Improvement of Saline and Alkali Soils,* U. S. Dept. of Agric. Handbook no. 60, 160 pp.

ROBERSON, C. E. and others, 1963, *Differences between Field and Laboratory Determinations of pH, Alkalinity, and Specific Conductivity of Natural Water,* U. S. Geol. Survey Prof. Paper 475-C, pp. 212-215.

ROBINSON, L. R., Jr., and DIXON, R. I., 1968, *Iron and Manganese Precipitation in Low Alkalinity Ground Waters,* Water & Sewage Works, v. 115, no. 11, Nov.

ROSSUM, J. R., 1948, *Chemical Quality of Underground Water Supplies,* Water and Sewage Works, v. 95, pp. 69-71.

SCHOELLER, M., 1963, *Recherches sur l'acquisition de la composition chimique des eaux souterraines,* Drouillard, Bordeaux, 231 pp.

SCHNEIDER, ROBERT, 1962, *An Application of Thermometry to the Study of Ground Water,* U. S. Geol. Survey Water Supply Paper 1544-B.

SCOFIELD, C. S., 1940, *Salt Balance in Irrigated Areas,* J. Agric. Res., v. 61, pp. 17-39.

SCHOFIELD, J. C., 1955, *Methods of Distinguishing Sea-Ground-Water from Hydrothermal Water,* New Zealand J. Sci and Technology, v. 37, pp. 597-602.

SEABER, P. R., 1962, *Cation Hydrochemical Facies of Ground Water in the Englishtown Formation, New Jersey,* U. S. Geol. Surv. Prof. Paper 450-B.

SEABER, P. R., 1965, *Variations in Chemical Character of Water in the Englishtown Formation, New Jersey,* U. S. Geol. Survey Prof. Paper 498-B, 35 pp.

SILIN-BEKCURIN, A. I., 1957, *Types of Hydrochemical Maps in Hydrology,* Internat. Assoc. Sci. Hydrology, General Assembly Toronto, Pub. 44, v. 2, p. 85.

SILIN-BEKCURIN, A. I., 1961, *Conditions of Formation of Saline Waters in Arid Zones;* in *Salinity Problems in the Arid Zones,* pp. 43-47, UNESCO, Paris.

SKOUGSTAD, M. W., and HORR, C. A., 1963, *Occurrence and Distribution of Strontium in Natural Water,* U. S. Geol. Survey Water Supply Paper 1496-D, pp. 55-97.

STALLMAN, R. W., 1965, *Steady One-Dimensional Fluid Flow in a Semi-Infinite Porous Medium with Sinusoidal Surface Temperature,* J. Geophys. Res., v. 70, no. 12, June.

STIFF, H. A., Jr., 1951, *The Interpretation of Chemical Water Analysis by Means of Patterns,* J. Petroleum Tech., pt. 15.

SUGISAKI, R., 1962, *Geochemical Study of Ground Water,* Nagoya University, Japan, J. Earth Sci., v. 10, pp. 1-33.

TAUSSIG, K., 1961, *Natural Groups of Ground Water and their Origin,* Mekoroth, Tel Aviv.

TAYLOR, F. B., 1963, *Significance of Trace Elements in Public, Finished Water Supplies,* J. Am. Water Works Assoc., v. 55, pp. 619-623.

THOMAS, H. E., 1949, *Sanitary Quality of Ground-Water Supplies,* The Sanitarian, v. 11, pp. 147-151.

TRAINER, F. W., 1968, *Temperature Profiles in Water Wells as Indicators of Bedrock Fractures,* U. S. Geol. Survey Research Prof. Paper 600-B, pp. B210-214.

TURCAN, A. N., Jr., and WINSLOW, A. G., 1970, *Quantitative Mapping of Salinity, Volume and Yield of Saline Aquifers using Borehole Geophysical Logs,* J. Water Resources Res., v. 6, no. 5, pp. 1478-1481, Oct.

U. S. DEPARTMENT OF HEALTH, EDUCATION, AND WELFARE, 1962, *Public Health Service Drinking Water Standards,* U. S. Public Health Service Pub. 956.

U. S. SALINITY LABORATORY, 1954, *Diagnosis and Improvement of Saline and Alkali Soils,* U. S. Dept. Agric. Handbook 60.

VAN LIER, J. A., 1959, *The Solubility of Quartz,* Kemink en Zoon, Utrecht, The Netherlands, 54 pp.

WARING, F. G., 1949, *Significance of Nitrate in Water Supplies,* J. Am. Water Works Assoc., v. 41, pp. 147.

WARNER, D. L., and DOTY, L. F., 1967, *Chemical Reaction between Recharge Water and Aquifer Water,* Symp. Haifa, Internat. Assoc. Sci. Hydrology, pp. 278-288.

WHITE, D. E., 1957, *Magmatic, Connate, and Metamorphic Waters,* Bull. Geol. Soc. Am., v. 68, pp. 1659-1682.

WHITE, D. E. and others, 1963, *Chemical Composition of Sub-Surface Waters,* Chap. F, in *Data of Geochemistry,* 6th ed., U. S. Geol. Survey Prof. Paper 440-F, 67 pp.

WHITE, D. E., 1965, *Saline Waters of Sedimentary Rocks,* in *Fluids in Subsurface Environments,* Am. Assoc. Petroleum Geol., Mem. 4, pp. 342-367.

WILCOX, L. V., 1948, *The Quality of Water for Irrigation Use,* U. S. Dept. Agric. Tech. Bull. 962, Washington, D. C., 40 pp.

WILCOX, L. V., 1955, *Classification and Use of Irrigation Waters,* U. S. Dept. Agric. Circ. 969, Washington, D. C., 19 pp.

WILCOX, L. V., 1962, *Salinity Caused by Irrigation,* J. Am. Water Works Assoc., v. 54, p. 217, Feb.

WINSLOW, J. D., 1962, *Effect of Stream Infiltration on Ground-Water Temperatures near Schenectady, N. Y.,* U. S. Geol. Survey Prof. Paper 450-C, Art. 111, pp. C125-C128.

WORLD HEALTH ORGANIZATION, 1961, *European Standards for Drinking Water,* Geneva, 52 pp.

WORLD HEALTH ORGANIZATION, 1963, *International Standards for Drinking Water,* Geneva, 206 pp.

YAALON, D. H., 1963, *On the Origin and Accumulation of Salts in Groundwater and in Soils of Israel,* Res. Council of Israel Bull., v. 11G, no. 3, pp. 105-131.

CONTAMINATION OF GROUND WATER

ANDERSEN, J. R., and DORNBUSH, J. N., 1967, *Influence of Sanitary Landfill on Ground Water Quality,* J. Am. Water Works Assoc., v. 59, p. 457, Apr.

BAARS, J. K., 1957, *Travel of Pollution and Purification en Route in Sandy Soils,* Bull. World Health Organ., v. 16, no. 4, pp. 727-747.

BAARS, J. K., 1957, *Pollution of Ground Water,* Internat. Assoc. Sci. Hydrology, General Assembly Toronto, Pub. 44, v. 2, pp. 279-289.

BAETSLE, L. H., and SOUFFRIAU, J., 1967, *Installation of Chemical Barriers in Aquifers and their Significance in Accidental Contamination,* in *Disposal of Radioactive Wastes into the Ground,* Internat. Atomic Energy Agency Conf., Vienna, May 29-June 2.

BAETSLE, L. H. and others, 1968, *Remedial Actions in Case of Groundwater Contamination of Sandy Aquifers* — Final Report, Centre d'Etude de l'Energie Nucleaire, Rept. EUR-4095, Mol, Belgium, also publ. in. Nuclear Sci. Abs., v. 23, 1969.

BROWN, R. H., 1964, *Hydrologic Factors Pertinent to Ground-Water Contamination,* Ground Water, v. 2, no. 1.

BUSH, A. F., 1954, *Studies of Waste Water Reclamation and Utilization,* Calif. State Water Pollution Control Bd., Pub. no. 9, Sacramento, Calif.

BUTLER, R. G. and others, 1954, *Underground Movement of Bacterial and Chemical Pollutants,* J. Am. Water Works Assoc., v. 46, pp. 97-111.

CALDWELL, E. L., 1938, *Pollution Flow from Pit Latrine when Permeable Soils of Considerable Depth Exist Below the Pit,* J. Infectious Diseases, v. 62, no. 3, pp. 225-258.

CALDWELL, E. L., and PARR, L. W., 1937, *Ground Water Pollution and the Bored-Hole Latrine,* J. Infectious Diseases, v. 61, no. 2, pp. 148-183.

CALDWELL, E. L., 1937, *Pollution Flow from Pit Latrines when Impervious Stratum closely Underlies the Flow,* J. Infectious Diseases, v. 61, no. 3, pp. 270-288.

CALDWELL, E. L., 1937, *Study of an Envelope Pit Privy,* J. Infectious Diseases, v. 61, no. 3, pp. 264-269.

COLLIER, C. R. and others, 1964, *Influences of Strip Mining on the Hydrologic Environment of Parts of Beaver Creek Basin, Kentucky, 1955-59,* U. S. Geol. Survey Prof. Paper 427-B, 83 pp.

CROSBY, J. W., III and others, 1968, *Migration of Pollutants in a Glacial Outwash Environment,* Water Resources Res., v. 4, no. 5, pp. 1095-1115.

DAVIDS, H. W., and LIEBER, MAXIM, 1951, *Underground Water Contamination by Chromium Wastes,* Water and Sewage Works, v. 98, no. 12, p. 528-534.

DEBUCHANNE, G. D., and LAMOREAUX, P. E., 1961, *Geologic Controls Related to Ground-Water Contamination,* in *Ground-Water Contamination,* Proc. 1961 Symp., U. S. Public Health Service Tech. Rept. W61-5, pp. 3-7.

DEUTSCH, MORRIS, 1963, *Groundwater Contamination and Legal Controls in Michigan,* U. S. Geol. Survey Water Supply Paper 1691.

DREWRY, W. A., and ELIASSEN, R., 1968, *Virus Movement in Ground Water,* J. Water Pollution Control Fed., v. 40, pp. R257-R272, Aug.

EMRICH, G. H., and MERRITT, G. L., 1969, *Effects of Mine Drainage on Ground Water,* Ground Water, v. 7, no. 3, p. 27.

ENGINEERING-SCIENCE, INC., 1961, *Effects of Refuse Dumps on Groundwater Quality,* Resources Agency Calif. State Water Pollution Control Board, Pub. 211.

FLYNN, J. M. and others, 1958, *Study of Synthetic Detergents in Ground Water,* J. Am. Water Works Assoc., v. 50, no. 12, pp. 1551-1562.

FUNGAROLI, A. A., and EMRICH, G. H., 1966, *Pollution of Subsurface Water by Sanitary Landfill,* Cooperative Study Civil Eng. Dept. Drexel Inst. of Technology and Bur. Sanitary Eng. Penn. Dept. of Health.

GERAGHTY, J. J., 1962, *Movements of Contaminants,* Water Well J., v. 16, Oct.

GOTAAS, H. B., 1953, *Laboratory and Field Investigations of the Travel of Pollution from Direct Water Recharge into Underground Formations,* Annual Report Sanitary Engineering Res. Projects, Univ. of California, Berkeley.

59

GOTAAS, H. B. and others, 1954, *Report on the Investigation of Travel of Pollution,* Calif. State Water Pollution Control Bd., Pub. no. 11, Sacramento, 218 pp.

GREENBERG, A. E., 1953, *Field Investigation of Waste Water Reclamation in Relation to Ground Water Pollution,* California State Water Pollution Bd., Pub. no. 6, Sacramento.

GRUBB, H. F., 1970, *Effects of a Concentrated Acid on Water Chemistry and Water Use in a Pleistocene Outwash Aquifer,* Ground Water, v. 8, no. 5, pp. 4-8.

KLAER, F. H., Jr., 1963, *Bacteriological and Chemical Factors in Induced Infiltration,* Ground Water, v. 1, no. 1.

KLIGLER, I. J., 1921, *Investigation of Soil Pollution and Relation of Various Types of Privies to the Spread of Intestinal Infections,* Rockeller Institute for Medical Res., Monograph 15.

KRUL, W. F. J. M., 1957, *Sanitary Engineering and Water Economy in Europe,* Bull. of the World Health Organization, v. 16, no. 4, Geneva.

LEGRAND, H. E., 1964, *Management Aspects of Groundwater Contamination,* J. Water Pollution Control Fed., v. 36, no. 9, pp. 1133-1145.

LEGRAND, H. E., 1964, *A system for Evaluating the Contamination Potential of Some Waste Sites,* J. Am. Water Works Assoc., v. 56, no. 8, pp. 959-974.

LEGRAND, H. E., 1965, *Patterns of Contaminated Zones of Water in the Ground,* Water Resources Res., v. 1, no. 1, pp. 83-95.

LIEBER, MAXIM and others, 1964, *Cadmium and Hexavalent Chromium in Nassau County Ground Water,* J. Am. Water Works Assoc., v. 56, no. 6, pp. 739-747.

MAXEY, G. B., and FARVOLDEN, R. N., 1965, *Hydrogeologic Factors in Problems of Contamination in Arid Lands,* Ground Water, v. 3, no. 4, pp. 29-32.

McMILLION, L. G., and HOUSER, VICTOR, 1969, *Field Evaluation of Potential Pollution from Ground-Water Recharge,* Water Well J., v. 23, no. 8, Aug.

NELSON, R. W., and ELIASON, J. R., 1966, *Prediction of Water Movement through Soils – a First Step in Waste Transport Analysis,* Proc. 21st Industrial Waste Conf., Purdue Univ. Engr. Ext. Bull. no. 121, v. 1, pp. 516-526.

NEW YORK STATE WATER POLLUTION CONTROL BOARD, 1969, *Effect of Synthetic Detergents on the Ground Waters of Long Island, New York,* New York State Water Pollution Control Board, Res. Rept. 6, 17 p.

NIGHTINGALE, H. I., 1970, *Statistical Evaluation of Salinity and Nitrate Content and Trends beneath Urban and Agricultural Areas – Fresno, California,* Ground Water, v. 8, no. 1, pp. 22-29.

ORLOB, G. T., and KRONE, R. B., 1956, *Movement of Coliform Bacteria Through Porous Media,* Sanitary Engineering Res. Lab., Univ. of California, Berkeley.

PERLMUTTER, N. M. and others, 1963, *Movement of Waterborne Cadmium and Hexavalent Chromium Wastes in South Farmingdale, Nassau County, Long Island, New York,* U. S. Geol. Survey Prof. Paper 475-C, pp. 179-184

PERLMUTTER, N. M., and LIEBER, MAXIM, 1970, *Dispersal of plating Wastes and Sewage Contaminants in Ground Water and Surface Water South Farmingdale-Massapequa Area, Nassau County,* New York, U. S. Geol. Survey Water Supply Paper 1879-G.

PERLMUTTER, N. M., and GUERRERA, A. A., 1970, *Detergents and Associated Contaminants in Ground Water at Three Public-Supply Well Fields in Southwestern Suffolk County, Long Island, New York,* U. S. Geol. Survey Water Supply Paper 2001-B, 22 pp.

QASIM, S. R., and BURCHINAL, J. C., 1970, *Leaching of Pollutants from Refuse Beds,* J. Sanitary Eng. Div. Am. Soc. Civil Engrs., v. 96, no. SA1, Feb.

ROBECK, G. G. and others, 1963, *Degradation of ABS and other Organics in Unsaturated Soils,* J. Water Pollution Control Fed., v. 35, pp. 1225-1237, Oct.

ROBBINS, J. W. D., and KRIZ, G. J., 1969, *Relation of Agriculture to Groundwater Pollution – a Review,* Trans. Am. Soc. Agr. Engrs., v. 12, no. 3, p. 397.

ROMERO, J. C., 1970, *The Movement of Bacteria and Viruses through Porous Media,* Ground Water, v. 8, no. 2, pp. 37-49.

SCALF, M. R. and others, 1968, *Fate of DDT and Nitrate in Ground Water,* U. S. Dept. Interior, Robert S. Kerr Water Res. Center, Ada, Oklahoma, 46 pp.

SCALF, M. R. and others 1969, *Movement of DDT and Nitrates During Ground-Water Recharge,* Water Resources Res., v. 5, no. 5, p. 1041.

STILES, C. W., 1927, *Experimental Bacterial and Chemical Pollution of Wells via Ground Water and the Factors Involved,* U. S. Public Health Service Hygiene Lab. Bull. 147.

SUESS, M. J., 1964, *Retardation of ABS in Different Aquifers,* J. Am. Water Works Assoc., v. 56, p. 89, Jan.

U. S. PUBLIC HEALTH SERVICE, 1961, *Proceedings of 1961 Symposium on Groundwater Contamination* – Cincinnati, Ohio, Tech. Rept. W61-5.

WALKER, T. R., 1961, *Ground Water Contamination in the Rocky Mountain Arsenal Area, Denver, Colorado,* Bull. Geol. Soc. America no. 72.

WALKER, W. H., 1969, *Illinois Ground Water Pollution,* J. Am. Water Works Assoc., v. 61, no. 1, pp. 31-40.

WALTON, GRAHAM, 1960, *ABS Contamination,* J. Am. Water Works Assoc., v. 52, p. 1354, Nov.

WALTON, GRAHAM, 1961, *Public Health Aspects of the Contamination of Ground Water in the Vicinity of Derby, Colorado,* Proc. Symp. Ground Water Contamination, Robert A. Taft San. Eng. Center, Tech. Rept. W61-5, Cincinnati, Ohio.

WATER WELL JOURNAL, 1970, *Primer on Ground Water Pollution,* Special Issue, Water Well J., v. 24, no. 7, July.

RADIONUCLIDES IN GROUND WATER

ARNDT, R. H., and KURODA, P. K., 1953, *Radioactivity of Rivers and Lakes in Parts of Garland and Hot Springs Counties, Arkansas,* Econ. Geol., v. 48, pp. 551-567.

AZIZ, A., and MUBARAK, M. A., 1968, *Ion Exchange Properties of Pinstech Soil for the Disposal of Liquid Radioactive Waste Directly into the Ground,* Rept. Pinstech/HP-7, Pakistan Inst. Nuclear Sci. and Technology, Islamabad, Pakistan, also in Nuclear Sci. Abs., 23, 21927 (1969).

BARKER, F. B., and SCOTT, R. C., 1958, *Uranium and Radium in the Ground Water of the Llano Estacado, Texas and New Mexico,* Trans. Am. Geophys. Union, v. 39, pp. 459-466.

BARKER, F. B., and SCOTT, R. C., 1961, *Uranium and Radium in Ground Water from Igneous Terranes of the Pacific Northwest,* U. S. Geol. Survey Prof. Paper 424-B, pp. 298-299.

BATZEL, R. E., 1960, *Radioactivity Associated with Underground Nuclear Explosions,* J. Geophys. Res., v. 65, pp. 2897-2902.

BELIN, R. E., 1959, *Radon in the New Zealand Geothermal Regions,* Geochim. et Cosmochim. Acta, v. 16, pp. 181-191.

BELTER, W. G., 1963, *Waste Management Activities of the U. S. Atomic Energy Commission,* Ground Water, v. 1, pp. 17-24.

BIERSCHENK, W. H., 1961, *Observational and Field Aspects of Ground-Water Flow at Hanford (Washington),* in *Ground Disposal of Radioactive Wastes,* Sanitary Engineering Res. Lab., Univ. of California, Berkeley, Conference Proc., pp. 147-156.

BOWEN, B. M. and others, 1960, *Geological Factors Affecting Ground Disposal of Liquid Radioactive Wastes into Crystalline Rocks at the Georgia Nuclear Laboratory Site,* Twenty-First Int. Geol. Congress Section 20, pp. 32-48.

BROWN, D. J., and RAYMOND, J. R., 1962, *Radiologic Monitoring of Ground Water at the Hanford Project,* J. Am. Water Works Assoc., v. 54, pp. 1201-1212.

CLEBSCH, ALFRED, Jr., *Tritium-Age of Ground Water at the Nevada Test Site, Nye County, Nevada,* U. S. Geol. Survey Prof. Paper 424-C, pp. 122-125.

DELAGUNA, WALLACE, 1962, *Engineering Geology of Radioactive Waste Disposal,* Geol. Soc. America, Reviews in Engineering Geology, v. 1, pp. 129-160.

FEDERAL CIVIL DEFENSE DIVISION, 1957, *Water Contaminated by Radioactive Fallout from Atomic Weapons,* Municipal Utilities, v. 99, no. 3, Toronto, Canada.

GILCREAS, F. W., 1961, *Radioactive Pollution of Water Supplies,* Water Works Engineering, v. 114, no. 3, New York.

HIGGINS, G. H., 1959, *Evaluation of the Ground-Water Contamination Hazard from Underground Nuclear Explosions,* J. Geophys. Res., v. 64, pp. 1509-1519.

JUDSON, SHELDON, and OSMOND, J. K., 1955, *Radioactivity in Ground and Surface Water*, Am. J. Sci., v. 253, pp. 104-116.

LANDIS, E. R., 1960, *Uranium Content of Ground and Surface Waters in a Part of the Central Great Plains*, U. S. Geol. Survey Bull. 1087-G, pp. 223-258.

LINDEROTH, C. E., and PEARCE, D. W., 1961, *Operating Practices and Experiences at Hanford (Washington)* in *Ground Disposal of Radioactive Wastes*, Sanitary Engineering Res. Lab., Univ. of California, Berkeley, Conference Proc., pp. 7-16.

MAZOR, E., 1962, *Radon and Radium Content of some Israeli Water Sources and a Hypothesis on Under-Ground Reservoirs of Brines, Oils, and Gases in the Rift Valley*, Geochim. et Cosmochim. Acta, v. 26, pp. 765-786.

MUNNICH, K. O., and VOGEL, J. C., 1960, C^{14} *Determination of Deep Ground-Waters*, Internat. Assoc. Sci. Hydrology, General Assembly of Helsinki, Pub. 52, pp. 537-541.

REICHERT, S. O., 1962, *Radionuclides in Ground Water at the Savannah River Plant Waste Disposal Facilities*, J. Geophys. Res., v. 67, pp. 4363-4374.

ROBINSON, B. P., 1962, *Ion-Exchange Minerals and Disposal of Radioactive Wastes-a Survey of Literature*, U. S. Geol. Survey Water Supply Paper 1616, 132 pp.

ROEDDER, EDWIN, 1959, *Problems in the Disposal of Acid Aluminum Nitrate High-Level Radioactive Waste Solutions by Injection into Deep-Lying Permeable Formations*, U. S. Geol. Survey Bull. 1088, 65 pp.

SCHMALZ, B. L., 1961, *Operating Practices, Experiences, and Problems at the National Reactor Testing Station, Idaho*, in *Ground Disposal of Radioactive Wastes*, Sanitary Eng. Res. Lab., Univ. of California, Berkeley, Conference Proc., pp. 17-33.

SCHROEDER, M. C., and JENNINGS, A. R., 1963, *Laboratory Studies of the Radioactive Contamination of Aquifers*, Univ. of California, Lawrence Radiation Lab. Pub. UCRL-13074, 51 pp. plus 66 pp. Appendices.

SCOTT, R. C., and BARKER, F. B., 1958, *Radium and Uranium in Ground Water in the United States*, Second United Nations Internat. Conference on Peaceful Uses of Atomic Energy, 10 pp.

SMITH, B. M. and others, 1961, *Natural Radioactivity in Ground Water Supplies in Maine and New Hampshire,* J. Am. Water Works Assoc., Jan.

STEAD, F. W., 1963, *Tritium in Ground Water around Large Underground Fusion Explosions,* Sci., v. 142, pp. 1163-1165.

THATCHER, L. and others, 1961, *Dating Desert Ground Water,* Sci., v. 134, pp. 105-106.

TOKAREV, A. N., and SHCHERBAKOV, A. V., 1956, *Radio-Hydrogeology,* Moscow, State Publ. of Sci.-Tech. Literature on Geol. and Conservation of Natl. Resources (English transl. by U. S. Atomic Energy Comm., AEC-tr-4100) 346 pp.

WILLIAMS, C. C., 1948, *Contamination of Deep Water Wells in Southeastern Kansas,* Kansas Geol. Survey Bull. 76, pt. 2, pp. 13-28.

SALT-WATER INTRUSION

ANONYMOUS, 1958, *Sea Water Intrusion in California,* State Dept. of Water Resources, Div. of Resources Planning, Bull. 63.

BANKS, H. O., and RICHTER, R. C., 1953, *Sea-Water Intrusion into Ground-Water Basins Bordering the California Coast and Inland Bays,* Trans. Am. Geophys. Union, v. 34, pp. 575-582.

BARKSDALE, H. C., 1940, *The Contamination of Ground-Water by Salt Water near Parlin, New Jersey,* Trans. Am. Geophys. Union, v. 21, pp. 471-474.

BAUMANN, P., 1953, *Experiments with Fresh-Water Barrier to Prevent Sea Water Intrusion,* J. Am. Water Works Assoc., v. 45, pp. 521-534.

BEAR, JACOB and TODD, D. K., 1960, *Transition Zone between Fresh and Salt Waters in Coastal Aquifers,* Hydraulic Lab., Univ. of California, Berkeley.

BEAR, JACOB, 1961, *Some Experiments in Dispersion,* Geophys. Res., v. 66.

BEAR, JACOB, and DAGAN, G., 1963, *Some Exact Solutions of Interface Problems by Means of the Hodograph Method,* J. Geophys. Res., v. 69.

BIEMOND, C., 1957, *Dune Water Flow and Replenishment in the Catchment Area of the Amsterdam Water Supply,* J. Inst. Water Engrs., v. 11, pp. 195-213.

BLACK, A. P. and others, 1953, *Salt Water Intrusion in Florida,* Florida Water Survey and Res. Paper no. 9, 38 pp.

BRAITHWAITE, F., 1855, *On the Infiltration of Salt Water into the Springs of Wells under London and Liverpool,* Proc. Inst. Civil Engrs., v. 14, pp. 507-523.

BRENNEKE, A. M., 1945, *Control of Salt-Water Intrusion in Texas,* J. Am. Water Works Assoc., v. 37, pp. 579-584.

BROWN, J. S., 1925, *A Study of Coastal Ground Water with Special Reference to Connecticut,* U. S. Geol. Survey Water Supply Paper 537, 101 pp.

BROWN, R. H., and PARKER, G. G., 1945, *Salt-Water Encroachment in Limestone of Silver Bluff, Miami, Florida,* Econ. Geol., v. 40, pp. 235-262.

BRUINGTON, A. E., 1969, *Control of Sea-Water Intrusion in a Ground Water Aquifer,* Ground Water, v. 7, no. 3, pp. 9-15.

CALIFORNIA DEPT. OF WATER RESOURCES, 1965, *Sea-Water Intrusion-Oxnard Plain of Ventura County,* Bull. 63-1.

CALIFORNIA DEPT. OF WATER RESOURCES, 1966, *Santa Ana Gap Salinity Barrier, Orange County,* Bull. 147-1.

CALIFORNIA DEPT. OF WATER RESOURCES, 1968, *Sea-Water Intrusion-Bolsa- Sunset Area,* Bull. 63-2.

CALIFORNIA DEPT. OF WATER RESOURCES, 1970, *Sea-Water Intrusion; Pismo-Guadelupe Area,* Bull. 63-3, 82 pp.

CARLSON, E. J., 1968, *Removal of Saline Water from Aquifers,* U. S. Bureau of Reclamation Res. Rept. no. 13.

CHILDS, E. C., 1950, *The Equilibrium of Rain-Fed Groundwater Resting on Deeper Saline Water – The Ghyben-Herzberg Lens,* J. Soil Sciences, v. 1, no. 2, pp. 173-181.

COOPER, H. H., Jr., 1959, *A Hypothesis Concerning the Dynamic Balance of Fresh Water and Salt Water in a Coastal Aquifer,* J. Geophys. Res. v. 64, no. 4.

COOPER, H. H., Jr. and others, 1964, *Sea Water in Coastal Aquifers, Relation of Salt Water to Fresh Ground Water,* U. S. Geol. Survey, Water Supply Paper 1613C, 84 p.

DAY, P. R., 1956, *Dispersion of a Moving Salt-Water Boundary Advancing through Saturated Sand,* Trans. Am. Geophys. Union, v. 37, pp. 595-601.

GHYBEN, W. (BADON), 1889, *Nota in verband met de voorgenomen putboring nabij Amsterdam,* Koninkl. Inst. Ing. Tijdschr., The Hague.

GLOVER, R. E., 1959, *The Pattern of Fresh-Water Flow in a Coastal Aquifer,* J. Geophys. Res., v. 64, no. 4.

HANSHAW, B. and others, 1965, *Relation of Carbon 14 Concentrations to Saline Water Contamination of Coastal Aquifers,* Water Resources Res., v. 1, no. 1, pp. 109-114.

HANTUSH, M. S., 1968, *Unsteady Movement of Fresh Water in Thick Unconfined Saline Aquifers,* Bull. Internat. Assoc. of Sci. Hydrology, June.

HARDER, J. A. and others, 1953, *Laboratory Research on Sea Water Intrusion into Fresh Ground-Water Sources and Methods of Its Prevention-Final Report,* Sanitary Eng. Res. Lab., Univ. California, Berkeley, 68 pp.

HARRIS, WILLIAM H., 1967, *Stratification of Fresh and Salt Water on Barrier Islands as a Result of Differences in Sediment Permeability,* Water Resources Res., v. 3, no. 1.

HAYAMI S., 1951, *On the Saline Disaster and Variation of Coastal Underground Water Caused by Land Subsidence Accompanying the Great Earthquake of December 21, 1947,* General Assembly Brussels, Internat. Assoc. Sci. Hydrology, v. 2, pp. 249-251.

HENRY, H. R., 1959, *Salt Intrusion into Fresh-Water Aquifers,* J. Geophys. Res., v. 64, no. 11.

HENRY, H. R., 1964, *Interfaces Between Salt Water and Fresh Water in Coastal Aquifers,* U. S. Geol. Survey Water Supply Paper, 1613-3.

HERZBERG, B., 1901, *Die Wasserversorgung einiger Nordseebader,* J. Gasbeleuchtung Wasserversorgung, v. 44.

JACOBS, M., and SCHMORAK, S., 1960, *Sea Water Intrusion and Interface Determination along the Coastal Plain of Israel,* Jerusalem Hydrological Service, v. 1, Hydrological Paper no. 6.

KOHOUT, F. A., 1960, *Cyclic Flow of Salt Water in the Biscayne Aquifer of Southeastern Florida,* J. Geophys. Res., v. 65, no. 7.

LAU, L. S., 1967, *Seawater Encroachment in Hawaiian Ghyben-Herzberg Systems,* Am. Water Resources Assoc., Proc. Symp. on Ground-Water Hydrology, San Francisco, Calif., pp. 259-271.

LAVERTY, F. B., and VAN DER GOOT, H. A., 1955, *Development of a Fresh-Water Barrier in Southern California for the Prevention of Sea Water Intrusion,* J. Am. Water Works Assoc., v. 47, pp. 886-908.

LEGGETTE, R. M., 1947, *Salt Water Encroachment in the Lloyd Sand on Long Island,* N. Y., Water Works Eng., v. 100, pp. 1076-1079, 1107-1109.

LIEFRINCK, F. A., 1930, *Water Supply Problems in Holland,* Public Works, v. 61, no. 9, pp. 19-20, 65-66, 69.

LOVE, S. K., 1944, *Cation-Exchange in Ground Water Contaminated with Sea Water near Miami, Florida,* Trans. Am. Geophys. Union, v. 25, pp. 951-955.

LUSCZYNSKI, N. J., 1961, *Head and Flow of Ground Water of Variable Density,* J. Geophys. Res., v. 66, no. 12.

LUSCZYNSKI, N. J., and SWARZENSKI, W. V., 1962, *Fresh and Salty Ground Water in Long Island, New York,* Proc. Am. Soc. Civil Engrs., v. 88, no. 3207, pp. 173-194.

LUSCZYNSKI, N. J., and SWARZENSKI, W. V., 1966, *Salt-Water Encroachment in Southern Nassau and Southeastern Queens Counties, Long Island, New York,* U. S. Geol. Survey Water Supply Paper 1613-F, 76 pp.

MAURIN, V., and ZOETL, J., 1967, *Salt-Water Encroachment in the Low Altitude Karst Water Horizons of the Island of Kephallinia (Ionic Islands),* in *Hydrology of Fractured Rocks,* Proc. Dubrovnik Symp. Oct. 1965, Internat. Assoc. Sci. Hydrology, Pub. 74, pp. 423-438.

NOMITSU, T. and others, 1927, *On the Contact Surface of Fresh-and Salt-Water near a Sandy Sea-Shore,* Mem. College Sci., Kyoto Imp. Univ. Ser. A., v. 10, no. 7, pp. 279-302.

OHRT, F., 1947, *Water Development and Salt Water Intrusion on Pacific Islands,* J. Am. Water Works Assoc., v. 39, pp. 979-988, Oct.

PARKER, G. G., 1945, *Salt-Water Encroachment in Southern Florida,* J. Am. Water Works Assoc., v. 37, pp. 526-542.

PENNINK, J. M. K., 1905, *Investigations for Ground-Water Supplies,* Trans. Am. Soc. Civil Engrs., v. 54-D, pp. 169-181.

PERLMUTTER, N. M. and others, 1959, *The Relation Between Fresh and Salty Ground Water in Southern Nassau and Southeastern Queens Counties, Long Island, New York,* Econ. Geol. v. 54, no. 3, pp. 416-435.

PERLMUTTER, N. M., and GERAGHTY, J. J., 1963, *Geology and Ground-Water Conditions in Southern Nassau and Southeastern Queens Counties, Long Island, N. Y.,* U. S. Geol. Survey Water Supply Paper 1613-A, 205 pp.

POLAND, J. F., 1943, *Saline Contamination of Coastal Ground Water in South California,* Western City, v. 19, pp. 46, 48, 50, Oct.

RADER, E. M., 1955, *Salt Water Encroachment into Well Water in the Miami Area,* Proc. Am. Soc. Civil Engrs. v. 81, sep. 669, 11 pp.

REVELLE, R., 1941, *Criteria for Recognition of Sea Water in Ground-Waters,* Trans. Am. Geophys. Union, v. 22, pp. 593-597.

RHODES, A. D., 1951, *Puddled-Clay Cutoff Walls Stop Sea-Water Infiltration,* Civil Eng., v. 21, no. 2, pp. 21-23.

RIDDEL, J. O., 1933, *Excluding Salt Water from Island Wells-A Theory of the Occurrence of Ground Water Based on Experience at Nassau, Bahama Islands,* Civil Eng., v. 3, pp. 383-385.

RUMER, R. R., Jr., and HARLEMAN, D. F., 1963, *Intruded Salt-Water Wedge in Porous Media,* J. Hydraul. Div. Am. Soc. Civil Engrs., v. 89, no. HY6, pp. 193-220.

RUMER, R. R., Jr., and SHIAU, J. C., 1968, *Salt Water Interface in a Layered Coastal Aquifer,* Water Resources Res., v. 4, no. 6, pp. 1235-1249.

SCHMORAK, S., 1967, *Salt Water Encroachment in the Coastal Plain of Israel,* Internat. Assoc. Sci. Hydrology, Haifa, Pub. 72, pp. 305-318.

SCHMORAK, S., and MERCADO, A., 1969, *Upconing of Fresh Water — Sea Water Interface Below Pumping Wells,* Water Resources Res., v. 5, no. 6, p. 1290.

SENIO, K., 1951, *On the Ground Water near the Seashore,* General Assembly Brussels, Internat. Assoc. Sci. Hydrology, v. 2, pp. 175-177.

SHECHTER, M., and SCHWARTZ, J., 1970, *Optimal Planning of a Coastal Collector,* Water Resources Res., v. 6, no. 4, pp. 1017-1025.

SIMPSON, T. R., 1946, *Salinas Basin Investigation,* Bull. 52, Calif. Div. Water Resources, Sacramento, 230 pp.

TASK COMMITTEE ON SALTWATER INTRUSION, 1969, *Saltwater Intrusion in the United States,* J. Hydraulics Div., Am. Soc. Civil Engrs., v. 95, no. HY5, Sept.

THOMPSON, D. G., 1933, *Some Relations between Ground-Water Hydrology and Oceanography,* Trans. Am. Geophys. Union, v. 14, pp. 30-33.

TODD, D. K., 1953, *An Abstract of Literature Pertaining to Sea Water Intrusion and its Control,* Tech. Bull. 10, Sanitary Eng. Res. Project, Univ. California, Berkeley, 74 pp.

TODD, D. K., 1953, *Sea-Water Intrusion in Coastal Aquifers,* Trans. Am. Geophys. Union, v. 34, pp. 749-754.

TOLMAN, C. F., and POLAND, J. F., 1940, *Ground-Water, Salt-Water Infiltration and Ground-Surface Recession in Santa Clara Valley, Santa Clara County, California,* Trans. Am. Geophys. Union, v. 21, pp. 23-35.

TOYOHARA, Y., 1935, *A Study on the Coastal Ground Water at Yumigahama, Tottori,* Mem. College Sci., Kyoto Imp. Univ. Ser. A., v. 18, no. 5, pp. 295-309.

TURNER, S. F., and FOSTER, M. D., 1934, *A Study of Salt-Water Encroachment in the Galveston Area, Texas,* Trans. Am. Geophys. Union, v. 15, pp. 432-435.

WENTWORTH, C. K., 1939, *The Specific Gravity of Sea Water and the Ghyben-Herzberg Ratio at Honolulu,* Bull. Univ. of Hawaii no. 8, v. 18, June.

WENTWORTH, C. K., 1942, *Storage Consequences of the Ghyben-Herzberg Theory,* Trans. Am. Geophys. Union, v. 23, pp. 683-693.

WENTWORTH, C. K., 1946, *Laminar Flow in the Honolulu Aquifer,* Trans. Am. Geophys. Union, v. 27, no. 4, pp. 540-548, Aug.

WENTWORTH, C. K., 1947, *Factors in the Behavior of Ground Water in a Ghyben-Herzberg System,* Pacific Sci., v. 1, pp. 172-184.

WENTWORTH, C. K., 1948, *Growth of the Ghyben-Herzberg Transition Zone under a Rinsing Hypothesis,* Trans. Am. Geophys. Union, v. 29, pp. 97-98.

WENTWORTH, C. K., 1951, *The Process and Progress of Salt-Water Encroachment,* Internat. Assoc. Sci. Hydrology, General Assembly Brussels, v. 2, pp. 238-248.

WELL DESIGN AND DRILLING METHODS

AHRENS, T. P., 1970, *Basic Considerations of Well Design,* Water Well J., (in 4 parts), Apr., pp. 45-50, May, pp. 49-52, June, pp. 47-51 and Aug., pp. 35-37.

AMERICAN WATER WORKS ASSOCIATION, 1967, *AWWA Standard for Deep Wells,* New York, transl. into Spanish by M. R. Llamas and A. Faura, (*Normas de la American Water Works Association para pozos profundos*), Servicio Geológico, Bull. no. 30, Madrid 1969, 115 pp.

ANONYMOUS, 1958, *Drilling Mud Data Book,* Baroid Div., National Lead Co., Houston, Texas.

ANONYMOUS, 1966, *Cable Tool Drilling Manual,* Sanderson Cyclone Drill Co., Orville, Ohio, 50 pp.

ANONYMOUS, 1967, *Blaster's Handbook,* E. I. du Pont de Nemours & Co., Inc., Wilmington, Del.

ANONYMOUS, 1969, *Well Drilling Manual,* Koehring, Speedstar Div., Enid, Okla.

BENNISON, E. W., 1953, *Fundamentals of Water Well Operation and Maintenance,* J. Am. Water Works Assoc., v. 45, pp. 252-258.

BLAIR, A. H., 1970, *Well Screens and Gravel Packs,* Ground Water, v. 8, no. 1.

BOWMAN, ISAIAH, 1911, *Well-Drilling Methods,* U. S. Geol. Survey Water Supply Paper 257.

BRANTLY, J. E., 1948, *Rotary Drilling Handbook,* Palmer Publications, Los Angeles, 565 pp.

BRANTLY, J. E., 1961, *Percussion-Drilling System,* in *History of Petroleum Engineering,* D. V. Carter (ed.), Am. Petroleum Inst., pp. 133-269.

BRANTLY, J. E., 1961, *Hydraulic Rotary-Drilling System* in *History of Petroleum Engineering,* D. V. Carter, (ed.), Am. Petroleum Inst., pp. 271-452.

CARLSTON, J. E., 1961, *Notes on the Early History of Water-Well Drilling in the United States,* Econ. Geology, v. 38, no. 2, pp. 119-136.

CATES, W. H., 1955, *Water Well Casing Manual,* U. S. Steel Pub. ADCWS-281-55, 44 pp.

CEDERSTROM, D. J., and TIBBITTS, G. C. Jr., 1961, *Jet Drilling in Fairbanks Area, Alaska,* U. S. Geol. Survey Water Supply Paper 1539-B, 28 pp.

CODE, W. E., 1949, *Rotary Method of Drilling Large Diameter Wells Using Reverse Circulation,* Water Well J., July-Aug.

CSALLANY, S., and WALTON, W. C., 1963, *Yields of Shallow Dolomite Wells in Northern Illinois,* Ill. State Water Survey Rept. of Invest. 46.

CUSHMAN, R. V. and others, 1953, *Geologic Factors Affecting Yield of Rock Wells in Southern New England,* J. New England Water Works Assoc., v. 67, pp. 77-93.

DAVIS, S. N. and TURK, L. J., 1964, *Optimum Depth of Wells in Crystalline Rock,* Ground Water, v. 2, no. 2.

DECKER, M. G., C 1968, *Cable Tool Fishing,* Water Well Publ. Co., Urbana, Ill.

ERICKSON, C. R., and WRIGHT, R. C., 1957, *Maintenance of Rock Wells,* J. Am. Water Works Assoc., June.

FEULNER, A. J., 1964, *Galleries and their Use for Development of Shallow Ground-Water Supplies, with Special Reference to Alaska,* U. S. Geol. Survey Water Supply Paper 1809-E, 16 pp.

GIEFER, G. J., 1963, *Water Wells; an Annotated Bibliography,* Water Resources Center, Archives ser. Rept. no. 13, Berkeley, Calif., 141 pp.

GORDON, R. W., 1958, *Water Well Drilling with Cable Tools,* Bucyrus-Erie Co., South Milwaukee, Wisc.

GOSSETT, O. C., 1958, *Reverse Circulation Rotary Drilling,* Water Well J., Nov.

GRIDLEY, H. K., 1952, *Installation and Performance of Radial Wells in Ohio River Gravel,* J. Am. Water Works Assoc., Dec.

GRIDLEY, H. K., and PAPADOPULOS, I. S., 1962, *Flow of Ground Water to Collector Wells,* Proc. Am. Soc. Civil Engrs., v. 88, no. HY5.

HANTUSH, M. S., 1961, *Economical Spacing of Interfering Wells,* in *Groundwater in Arid Zones,* Internat. Assoc. Sci. Hydrology, Pub. no. 57, pp. 350-364.

JANN, R. H., 1966, *Method for Deep Well Alignment Tests,* J. Am. Water Works Assoc., v. 58, p. 440, Apr.

JOHNSTON, C. N., 1951, *Irrigation Wells and Well Drilling,* Agric. Exp. Sta. Circ. 404, Univ. California, Berkeley, 32 pp.

KOOPMAN, F. C. and others, 1962, *Use of Inflatable Packers in Multiple-Zone Testing of Water Wells,* U. S. Geol. Survey Research, Prof. Paper 450-B, pp. B108-109.

KRUSE, GORDON, 1960, *Selection of Gravel Packs for Wells in Unconsolidated Aquifers,* Tech. Bull. 66, Colorado State Univ., Fort Collins, Colorado.

MACHIS, ALFRED, 1946, *Experimental Observations on Grouting Sands and Gravels,* Proc. Am. Soc. Civil Engrs., pp. 1207, 1218, 1226 and 1227, Nov.

MAURER, W. C., 1968, *Novel Drilling Techniques,* Pergamon Press Inc. Elmsford, New York and Oxford, England, 124 pp.

MEYER, G., and WYRICK, G. G., 1966, *Regional Trends in Water Well Drilling in the United States,* U. S. Geol. Survey Circ. 533, 8 pp.

MOGG, J. L., 1963, *The Technical Aspects of Gravel Well Construction,* J. New Eng. Water Works Assoc., v. 77, pp. 155-164.

MOSS, ROSCOE, Jr., 1958, *Water Well Construction in Formation Characteristics of the Southwest,* J. Am. Water Works Assoc., v. 50, p. 777, June.

OIL AND GAS JOURNAL, 1959, *Driller's Handbook,* Reprints from Oil and Gas J., Tulsa, Okla.

PILLSBURY, A. F., and CHRISTIANSEN, J. E., 1947, *Installing Ground-Water Piezometers by Jetting for Drainage Investigations,* Agric. Eng., v. 28, pp. 409-410.

PLUMB, C. E., and WELSH, J. L., 1955, *Abstract of Laws and Recommendations Concerning Water Well Construction and Sealing in the United States,* Water Quality Invest. Rept. 9, California Div. Water Resources, Sacramento, 391 pp.

REPUBLIC STEEL CORPORATION, 1965, *Standard and Line Pipe,* Cleveland, Ohio, 52 pp.

SCHWALEN, H. C., 1925, *The Stovepipe or California Method of Well Drilling as Practiced in Arizona,* Bull. 112, Univ. Arizona Agric. Exp. Sta., Tucson, pp. 103-154.

73

SERVICIO GEOLOGICO DE OBRAS PUBLICAS, INSTITUTO NACIONAL DE COLONIZACION, CENTRO DE ESTUDIOS INVESTIGACION Y APLICACIONES DEL AGUA, 1968, *Primer seminario de técnicas modernas para la construcción de pozos ponencias,* C.E.I.A.A., Barcelona, 529 pp.

SMITH, H. F., 1958, *Gravel Packing Water Wells,* Water Well J., v. 8, nos. 1 and 2.

SMITH, L. A., 1941, *Deep Wells in Sandstone Rock,* Water Works Eng., v. 94, pp. 710-712.

SMITH, R. C., 1963, *Relation of Screen Design of Mechanically Efficient Wells,* J. Am. Water Works Assoc., v. 55, no. 5, pp. 609-614.

SPIRIDONOFF, S. V., 1964, *Design and Use of Radial Collector Wells,* J. Am. Water Works Assoc., June.

STEVENS, P. R., 1963, *Examination of Drill Cuttings and Application of Resulting Information to Solving of Field Problems on the Navajo Indian Reservation, New Mexico and Arizona,* U. S. Geol. Survey Water Supply Paper 1544-H.

STONE, R., 1954, *Infiltration Galleries,* Proc. Am. Soc. Civil Engrs. v. 80, sep. 472, 12 pp.

THEIS, C. V., 1957, *The Spacing of Pumped Wells,* U. S. Geol. Survey, Ground Water Notes, Hydraulics, no. 31, open-file rept.

TODD, D. K., 1955, *Discussion of Infiltration Galleries,* Proc. Am. Soc. Civil Engrs., v. 81, sep. 647, pp. 7-9.

U. S. DEPARTMENT OF THE ARMY, 1957, *Wells,* Tech. Manual TM 5-297, U. S. Govt. Printing Office, Washington, D. C., 264 pp.

VAADIA, YOASH and SCOTT, V. H., 1958, *Hydraulic Properties of Perforated Well Casings,* Proc. Am. Soc. Civil Engrs., Irrig. and Drainage Div., Paper 1505, Jan.

WALTON, W. C., and CSALLANY, S., 1962, *Yields of Deep Sandstone Wells in Northern Illinois,* Ill. State Water Survey Rept. of Invest. 43.

WELL MAINTENANCE AND STIMULATION

BARNES, IVAN, and CLARKE, F. E., 1969, *Chemical Properties of Ground Water and their Corrosion and Encrustation Effects on Wells,* U. S. Geol. Survey Prof. Paper 498-D.

BENNISON, E. W., 1953, *Fundamentals of Water Well Operation and Maintenance,* J. Am. Water Works Assoc., March.

BLAKELEY, L. E., 1945, *The Rehabilitation, Cleaning, and Sterilization of Water Wells,* J. Am. Water Works Assoc., v. 37, pp. 101-114.

BRIGGS, G. F., 1949, *Corrosion and Incrustation of Well Screens,* J. Am. Water Works Assoc., Jan.

BROWN, F. D., 1942, *Restoring Well Capacity with Chlorine,* J. Am. Water Works Assoc., v. 34, no. 5, pp. 698-702.

CLARKE, FRANK, and BARNES, IVAN, 1965, *Study of Water-Well Corrosion, Chad Basin, Nigeria,* U. S. Geol. Survey, Open file Rept.

DEWITT, M. M., 1947, *How to Acidize Water Wells,* American City, v. 62, no. 10, pp. 92-93.

EBAUGH, R. M., 1950, *Water Well Redevelopment by Explosives,* J. Am. Water Works Assoc., Feb.

ERICKSON, C. R., 1961, *Cleaning Methods for Deep Wells and Pumps,* J. Am. Water Works Assoc., Feb.

GROOM, C. H., and BROWNING, J. T., 1947, *Water Well Acidizing,* Water Well J., v. 1, no. 1, pp. 9-11.

HARDER, E. C., 1919, *Iron-Depositing Bacteria and their Geological Relations,* U. S. Geol. Survey Prof. Paper 113, 85 pp.

KELLY, S. F., 1939, *Photographing Rock Walls and Casings of Boreholes,* Trans. Am. Geophys. Union, v. 20, pp. 269-271.

KLEBER, J. P., 1950, *Well Cleaning with Calgon,* J. Am. Water Works Assoc., v. 42, pp. 481-484.

KOENIG, LOUIS, 1960, *Survey and Analysis of Well Stimulation Performance,* J. Am. Water Works Assoc., v. 52, p. 333, Mar.

KOENIG, LOUIS, 1960, *Economic Aspects of Water Well Stimulation,* J. Am. Water Well Assoc., v. 52, p. 631, May.

KOENIG, LOUIS, 1960, *Effects of Stimulation on Well Operating Costs and its Performance on Old and New Wells,* J. Am. Water Well Assoc., v. 52, p. 1499, Dec.

KOENIG, LOUIS, 1961, *Relation between Aquifer Permeability and Improvement Achieved by Well Stimulation,* J. Am. Water Works Assoc., v. 53, p. 652, May.

MCCOMBS, J., and FIEDLER, A. G., 1928, *Methods of Exploring and Repairing Leaky Artesian Wells,* U. S. Geol. Survey Water Supply Paper 596, pp. 1-32.

MILAEGER, R. E., 1942, *Development of Deep Wells by Dynamiting,* J. Am. Water Works Assoc., v. 34, pp. 684-690.

MYLANDER, H. A., 1952, *Well Improvement by use of Vibratory Explosives,* J. Am. Water Works Assoc., v. 44, pp. 39-48.

ONGERTH, H. J., 1942, *Sanitary Construction and Protection of Wells,* J. Am. Water Works Assoc., v. 34, pp. 671-677.

WHITE, H. L., 1942, *Rejuvenating Wells with Chlorine,* Civil Eng., v. 12, pp. 263-265.

PUMPING EQUIPMENT

AMERICAN WATER WORKS ASSOCIATION, 1961, *American Standard Specifications for Vertical Turbine Pumps,* (ASA B58. 1; AWWA E101), J. Am. Water Works Assoc., v. 53, p. 333, Mar.

ANONYMOUS, 1954, *The Vertical Pump,* Johnston Pump Co., Pasadena, Calif.

ANONYMOUS, 1962, *Vertical Turbine Pump Facts,* Vertical Turbine Pump Assoc., Pasadena, Calif.

ANONYMOUS, 1970, *Pump Fundamentals,* Goulds Pumps, Inc., Seneca Falls, N. Y.

ANONYMOUS, 1970, *Application Manual for Large Submersible Pumps,* Red Jacket Mfg. Co., Davenport, Iowa.

76

ERICKSON, C. R., 1960, *Submersible Water Well Pumps,* J. Am. Water Works Assoc., Sep.

HICKS, T. G., 1954, *Handbook on Pumps,* Power, Oct., McGraw-Hill Book Co. Inc., New York.

HICKS, T. G., 1957, *Pump Selection and Application,* McGraw-Hill Book Co., New York, 422 pp.

HICKS, T. G., 1958, *Pump Operation and Maintenance,* McGraw-Hill Book Co. Inc., New York, 310 pp.

WASSON, R. H., 1968, *Industrial Pump Manual,* v. 1 and 2, Fairbanks, Morse and Co., Kansas City, Kansas.

ARTIFICIAL RECHARGE, RIVER
INFILTRATION AND STORAGE

ABERBACH, S. H., and SELLINGER, A., 1967, *Review of Artificial Ground-Water Recharge in the Coastal Plain of Israel,* Internat. Assoc. Sci. Hydrology, Symp. Haifa, v. 12, no. 1, pp. 65-77.

AMERICAN WATER WORKS ASSOCIATION, 1967, *Artificial Ground Water Recharge,* Task Group Rept., J. Am. Water Works Assoc., v. 59, p. 103, Jan.

ANONYMOUS, 1957, *Artificial Recharge Experiments at McDonald Well Field, Amarillo, Texas,* State Bd. of Water Engrs. Bull. 570.

ARNOLD, C. E. and others, 1949, *Report upon the Reclamation of Water from Sewage and Industrial Wastes in Los Angeles County, California,* Los Angeles County Flood Control District, Los Angeles, 159 pp.

BABCOCK, H. M., and CUSHING, E. M., 1942, *Recharge to Ground Water from Floods in a Typical Desert Wash, Pinal County, Arizona,* Trans. Am. Geophys. Union, v. 23, pp. 49-56.

BAFFA, J. J. and others, 1958, *Developments in Artificial Ground-Water Recharge,* J. Am. Water Works Assoc., v. 50, no. 7, p. 812-871.

BAFFA, J. J., 1970, *Injection Well Experience at Riverhead, N. Y.,* J. Am. Water Works Assoc., v. 62, no. 1, Jan.

BANKS, H. O. and others, 1954, *Artificial Recharge in California, Calif.* Div. of Water Resources, Sacramento, 41 pp.

BARKSDALE, H. C., and DE BUCHANANNE, G. D., 1946, *Artificial Recharge of Productive Ground-Water Aquifers in New Jersey,* Econ. Geology, v. 41, no. 7, pp. 726-737.

BAUMANN, P., 1952, *Ground-Water Movement Controlled through Spreading,* Trans. Am. Soc. Civil Engrs., v. 117, pp. 1024-1074.

BAUMANN, P., 1955, *Ground Water Phenomena Related to Basin Recharge,* Proc. Am. Soc. Civil Engrs., v. 81, sep. 806, 25 pp.

BAUMANN, P., 1963, *Theoretical and Practical Aspects of Well Recharge,* Trans. Am. Soc. Civil Engrs., v. 128, pt. I, pp. 739-764.

BEHNKE, JEROLD J., 1969, *Clogging in Surface Spreading Operations for Artificial Ground-Water Recharge,* Water Resources Res., v. 5, no. 4, p. 870.

BEREND, J. E. and others, 1967, *Use of Storm Runoff for Artificial Recharge,* Trans. Am. Soc. Agric. Engrs. v. 10, no. 5.

BETTAQUE, R. H. G., 1958, *Studien zur künstlichen Grundwasseranreicherung,* Pub. Inst. Siedlungswasserwirtschaft, v. 2, Techn. Hochschule, Hanover, 105 pp.

BIEMOND, C., 1957, *Dune Water Flow and Replenishment in the Catchment Area of the Amsterdam Water Supply,* J. Inst. Water Engrs., v. 11, pp. 195-213.

BITTINGER, M. W., and TRELEASE, F. J., 1960, *The Development and Dissipation of a Ground-Water Mound beneath a Spreading Basin,* Winter Meeting of Am. Soc. Agric. Engrs., Memphis, Tenn., Dec. 4-7.

BLISS, E. S., and JOHNSON, C. E., 1952, *Some Factors Involved in Ground-Water Replenishment,* Trans. Am. Geophys. Union, v. 33, pp. 547-558.

BOULTON, N. S., 1942, *The Steady Flow of Ground Water to a Pumped Well in the Vicinity of a River,* The Philosophical Magazine, v. 7, pp. 34-50.

BRASHEARS, M. L., Jr., 1946, *Artificial Recharge of Ground Water on Long Island, New York,* Econ. Geol., v. 41, pp. 503-516.

BRASHEARS, M. L., Jr., 1953, *Recharging Ground-Water Reservoirs with Wells and Basins,* Min. Eng., v. 5, pp. 1029-1032.

BRICE, H. D. and others, 1959, *A Progress Report on the Disposal of Storm Water at an Experimental Seepage Basin near Mineola, New York,* U. S. Geol. Survey open-file rept., 34 p.

BUCHAN, S., 1955, *Artificial Replenishment of Aquifers,* J. Inst. Water Engrs., v. 9, pp. 111-163.

CEDERSTROM, D. J., 1947, *Artificial Recharge of a Brackish Water Well,* The Commonwealth, Virginia Chamber of Commerce, Richmond, Dec.

CHRISTIANSEN, J. E., and MAGISTAD, O. C., 1945, *Report for 1944- Laboratory Phases of Cooperative Water-Spreading Study,* U. S. Regional Salinity Lab., Riverside, Calif., 74 pp.

CLYDE, G. D., 1951, *Utilization of Natural Underground Water Storage Reservoirs,* J. Soil and Water Conser., v. 6, pp. 15-19.

CLYMA, WAYNE, 1964, *Artificial Groundwater Recharge by a Multiple-Purpose Well,* Texas Agric. Exp. Sta., Misc. Pub. 712.

COHEN, PHILIP, and DURFOR, C. N., 1966, *Design and Construction of a Unique Injection Well on Long Island, New York,* U. S. Geol. Survey Prof. Paper 550-D, p. D253-D257.

COHEN, PHILIP and DURFOR, C. N., 1967, *Artificial-Recharge Experiments Utilizing Renovated Sewage-Plant Effluent — a Feasibility Study at Bay Park, New York,* Internat. Assoc. Sci. Hydrology Pub. 72, p. 194-199.

CONKLING, H., 1946, *Utilization of Ground-Water Storage in Stream-System Developments,* Trans. Am. Soc. Civil Engrs., v. 111, pp. 275-354.

COOPER, H. H., JR., and RORABAUGH, M. I., 1963, *Groundwater Movements and Bank Storage due to Flood Stages in Surface Streams,* U. S. Geol. Survey Water Supply Paper 1536-J.

DEUTSCH, MORRIS, 1967, *Artificial Recharge Induced by Interaquifer Leakage,* Internat. Assoc. Sci. Hydrology, Pub. 72, pp. 159-172.

DE WIEST, R. J. M., 1963 and 1964, *Replenishment of Aquifers Intersected by Streams,* J. Am. Soc. Civil Engrs., Hydraulics Div., Nov., 1963, pp. 165-191; Sept., 1964, pp. 161-168.

DIRECTO, L. S., and LINDAHL, M. E., 1969, *River Water Quality for Artificial Recharge,* J. Am. Water Works Assoc., v. 61, p. 175, Apr.

ERICKSON, E. T., 1949, *Using Runoff for Ground-Water Recharge,* J. Am. Water Works Assoc., v. 41, pp. 647-649.

ESMAIL, O. J., and KIMBLER, O. K., 1967, *Investigation of the Technical Feasibility of Storing Fresh Water in Saline Aquifers,* Water Resources Res., v. 3, no. 3, 683-695.

79

FERRIS, J. G., 1950, *Water Spreading and Recharge Wells,* Proc. Indiana Water Conserv. Conf., Ind. Dept. Conserv., Div. Water Resources, Indianapolis, pp. 52-59.

FRANKEL, J. R., 1967, *Economics of Artificial Recharge for Municipal Water Supply,* Symp. Haifa, Internat. Assoc. Sci. Hydrology Pub. no. 72; also Resources for the Future, Inc., Reprint no. 62, Mar. 1967.

FREEMAN, V. M., 1936, *Water-Spreading as Practiced by the Santa Clara Water-Conservation District, Ventura County, Calif.,* Trans. Am. Geophys. Union, v. 17, pp. 465-471.

GLOVER, R. E., and BALMER, G. G., 1954, *River Depletion Resulting from Pumping a Well near a River,* Trans. Am. Geophys. Union, v. 35, pp. 468-470.

GOTAAS, H. B. and others, 1953, *Final Report on Field Investigation and Research on Waste Water Reclamation and Utilization in Relation to Underground Water Pollution,* Calif. State Water Pollution Control Board, Pub. 6, 124 pp.

GOUDEY, R. F., 1931, *Reclamation of Treated Sewage,* J. Am. Water Works Assoc., v. 23, pp. 230-240.

GREEN, D. W. and others, 1966, *Storage of Fresh Water in Underground Reservoirs Containing Saline Water — Phase 1,* Kansas State Univ. Water Resources Res. Inst. Contrib. no. 3, *Phase 2,* Contrib. no. 36, 1970.

GREENBERG, A. E., and GOTAAS, H. B., 1952, *Reclamation of Sewage Water,* Am. J. Public Health, v. 42, pp. 401-410.

GUYTON, W. F., 1946, *Artificial Recharge of Glacial Sand and Gravel with Filtered River Water at Louisville, Kentucky,* Econ. Geol., v. 41, pp. 644-658.

HANTUSH, M. S., 1959, *Analysis of Data from Pumping Wells near a River,* J. Geophys. Res., v. 64, pp. 1921-1932.

HANTUSH, M. S., 1967, *Depletion of Flow in Right-Angle Stream Bends by Steady Wells,* Water Resources Res., v. 3, no. 1, pp. 235-240.

HANTUSH, M. S., 1967, *Growth and Decay of Ground-Water Mounds in Response to Uniform Percolation,* Water Resources Res., v. 3, no. 1.

HARMESON, R. H. and others, 1968, *Coarse Media Filtration for Artificial Recharge,* J. Am. Water Works Assoc., v. 60, no. 12, pp. 1396-1404.

HARPAZ, Y., and BEAR, J., 1964, *Investigations on Mixing of Waters Underground Storage Operations,* Internat. Assoc. Sci. Hydrology, Pub. 64, pp. 132-153.

HARPAZ, Y., 1965, *Field Experiments in Recharge and Mixing through Wells*, TAHAL, P. N. 483, Tel Aviv.

HASKELL, E. E., Jr., and BIANCHI, W. C., 1965, *Development and Dissipation of Ground Water Mounds beneath Square Recharge Basins*, J. Am. Water Works Assoc., v. 57, no. 3, pp. 349-353.

HAUSER, V. L., and LOTSPEICH, F. B., 1968, *Treatment of Playa Lake Water for Recharge through Wells*, Trans. Am. Soc. Agr. Engrs., v. 11, no. 1, pp. 108-111.

HERBERT, ROBIN, 1969, *Solving Multiwell, River Ground-Water Flow Problems*, J. Hydrology, v. 4, art. 420, pp. 30-38.

HUISMAN, L., 1957, *The Determination of the Geo-Hydrological Constants for Dune-Water Catchment Area of Amsterdam*, Internat. Assoc. Sci. Hydrology Pub. 44, v. 2, pp. 168-182.

HUISMAN, L., and VAN HAAREN, F. W. J., 1966, *Treatment of Water before Infiltration and Modification of its Quality during its Passage Underground*, Internat. Water Supply Congr., Barcelona, Spec. Paper no. 3.

HUNT, G. W., 1940, *Description and Results of Operations of the Santa Clara Valley Water Conservation District's Project*, Trans. Am. Geophys. Union, v. 21, pp. 13-23.

INTERNATIONAL ASSOCIATION OF SCIENTIFIC HYDROLOGY, 1970, *Artificial Groundwater Recharge – International Survey of Existing Water Recharge Facilities*, Internat. Assoc. Sci. Hydrology, Pub. 87, 762 pp.

JANSA, O. V., 1952, *Artificial Replenishment of Underground Water*, Internat. Water Supply Assoc., Second Cong., 105 pp., Paris.

JANSA, O. V., 1954, *Artificial Ground-Water Supplies of Sweden*, Internat. Assoc. Sci. Hydrology Rept. no. 2, Pub. no. 37, pp. 269-275.

JEFFORDS, R. M., 1945, *Recharge to Water-Bearing Formations along the Ohio Valley*, J. Am. Water Works Assoc., v. 37.

JENKINS, C. T., 1968, *Techniques for Computing Rate and Volume of Stream Depletion by Wells*, Ground Water, v. 6, pp. 37-46.

JENKINS, C. T., and HOFSTRA, W. E., 1970, *Availability of Water for Artificial Recharge, Plains Ground Water Management District, Colorado*, Colo. Water Conserv. Bd. Ground-Water Ser. Circ. 13, 16 pp.

JOHNSON, A. H., 1948, *Ground-Water Recharge on Long Island*, J. Am. Water Works Assoc., v. 40, pp. 1159-1166.

JOHNSON, A. I. and others, 1966, *Laboratory Study of Aquifer Properties and Well Design for an Artificial Recharge Site,* U. S. Geol. Survey Water Supply Paper 1615-H.

KATZ, D. L., and COATS, K. H., 1968, *Underground Storage of Fluids,* Ulrich's Books, Inc., Ann Arbor, Mich., 575 pp.

KATZ, D. L., and TEK, M. R., 1970, *Storage of Natural Gas in Saline Aquifers,* J. Water Resources Res., v. 6, no. 5, pp. 1515-1521, Oct.

KAZMANN, R. G., 1947, *Discussion of Apparent Changes in Water Storage during Floods at Peoria, Ill.,* Trans. Am. Geophys. Union, v. 28.

KAZMANN, R. G., 1948, *River Infiltration as a Source of Ground-Water Supply,* Trans. Am. Soc. Civil Engrs., v. 113, pp. 404-424.

KAZMANN, R. G., 1948, *The Induced Infiltration of River Water to Wells,* Trans. Am. Geophys. Union, v. 29, pp. 85-92.

KAZMANN, R. G., 1960, *Discussion of Paper by M. S. Hantush, Analysis of Data from Pumping Wells near a River,* J. of Geophys. Res., v. 65, pp. 1625-1626.

KLAER, F. H., Jr., 1953, *Providing Large Industrial Water Supplies by Induced Infiltration,* Min. Eng., v. 5, pp. 620-624.

LANE, D. A., 1934, *Surface Spreading-Operations by the Basin-Method and Tests on Underground Spreading by Means of Wells,* Trans. Am. Geophys. Union, v. 15, pp. 523-527.

LAVERTY, F. B., 1946, *Correlating Flood Control and Water Supply, Los Angeles Coastal Plain,* Trans. Am. Soc. Civil Engrs., v. 111, pp. 1127-1158.

LAVERTY, F. B., 1952, *Ground-Water Recharge,* J. Am. Water Works Assoc., v. 44, pp. 677-681.

LAVERTY, F. B., 1954, *Water-Spreading Operations in the San Gabriel Valley,* J. Am. Water Works Assoc., v. 46, pp. 112-122.

LEGGETTE, R. M., and BRASHEARS, M. L., Jr., 1938, *Groundwater for Air-Conditioning on Long Island, New York,* Trans. Am. Geophys. Union, v. 19, pp. 412-418.

LEHR, J. H., 1965, *Relation of Shape of Artificial-Recharge Pits to Infiltration Rate,* J. Am. Water Works Assoc., v. 56, p. 699, June.

LI, A. D. and others, 1969, *Evaluation of the Suitability of Water for Injection into Strata,* Tr. Tatar Neft. (USSR), 9, 299 (1966); Chem. Abs. 71, 69786 (1969).

LINDENBERGH, P. C., 1951, *Drawing Water from a Dune Area,* J. Am. Water Works Assoc., v. 43, pp. 713-724.

MARLETTE, R. R., 1967, *Artificial Recharge through Injection Wells in a Sandstone Aquifer,* Proc. Internat. Assoc. Sci. Hydrology, Gen. Assembly Bern.

MATHER, J. R., 1953, *The Disposal of Industrial Effluent by Woods Irrigation,* Trans. Am. Geophys. Union, v. 34, pp. 227-239.

MEINZER, O. E., 1946, *General Principles of Artificial Ground-Water Recharge,* Econ. Geol. v. 41, pp. 191-201.

MERCADO, A., 1967, *The Spreading Pattern of Injected Water in a Permeability Stratified Aquifer,* Internat. Assn. Sci. Hydrology, (Symp. of Haifa), Pub. 72, pp. 23-36.

MIKELS, F. C., and KLAER, F. H., JR., 1956, *Application of Ground Water Hydraulics to the Development of Water Supplies by Induced Infiltration,* Symposia Darcy, Internat. Assoc. Sci. Hydrology, Pub. 41, pp. 232-242.

MIKELS, F. C., 1952, *Report on Hydrogeological Survey for City of Zion, Illinois,* Ranney Method Water Supplies Inc., Columbus, Ohio.

MITCHELSON, A. T., and MUCKEL, D. C., 1937, *Spreading Water for Storage Underground,* U. S. Dept. Agric. Tech. Bull. 578, Washington, D. C., 80 pp.

MOORE, J. E., and JENKINS, C. T., 1966, *An Evaluation of the Effect of Groundwater Pumpage on the Infiltration rate of a Semipervious Streambed,* Water Resources Res., v. 2, no. 4, pp. 691-696.

MOULDER, E. A., and FRAZOR, D. R., 1957, *Artificial-Recharge Experiments at McDonald Well Field, Amarillo, Texas,* Bull. Texas Board Water Eng. no. 5701.

MOULDER, E. A., 1970, *Freshwater Bubbles: a Possibility for Using Saline Aquifers to Store Water,* J. Water Resources Res., v. 6, no. 5, pp. 1528-1531, Oct.

MUCKEL, D. C., 1953, *Research in Water Spreading,* Trans. Am. Soc. Civil Engrs., v. 118, pp. 209-219.

MUCKEL, D. C., 1959, *Replenishment of Ground-Water Supplies by Artificial Means,* Tech. Bull. 1195, U. S. Dept. Agric., Washington, D. C.

PRICE, C. E., 1961, *Artificial Recharge through a Well Tapping Basalt Aquifers Walla Walla Area, Washington,* U. S. Geol. Survey Water Supply Paper 1594-A, 33 pp.

RAFTER, G. W., 1897 and 1899, *Sewage Irrigation,* U. S. Geol. Survey Water Supply Papers 3 and 22, 100 and 100 pp.

RAHMAN, M. A. and others, 1969, *Effect of Sediment Concentration on Well Recharge in a Fine Sand Aquifer,* Water Resources Res., v. 5, no. 3, p. 641.

REBHUN, M., and SCHWARTZ, J., 1968, *Clogging and Contamination Processes in Recharge Wells,* Water Resources Res. v. 4, no. 6, pp. 1207-1219.

REED, J. E. and others, 1966, *Induced Recharge of an Artesian Glacial Drift Aquifer at Kalamazoo, Mich.,* U. S. Geol. Survey Water Supply Paper 1594-D, 62 pp.

RICHERT, J. G., 1900, *On Artificial Underground Water,* C. E. Fritze's Royal Bookstore, Stockholm, 33 pp.

ROPER, R. M., 1939, *Ground-Water Replenishment by Surface Water Diffusion,* J. Am. Water Works Assoc., v. 31, pp. 165-179.

RORABAUGH, M. I., 1951, *Stream-bed Percolation in Development of Water Supplies,* Trans. General Assembly Brussels, Internat. Assoc. Sci. Hydrology, v. 2, pp. 165-174; also U. S. Geol. Survey Ground Water Note 25, 1951.

RORABAUGH, M. I., 1956, *Ground-water Resources of the Northeastern Part of the Louisville Area, Kentucky,* U. S. Geol. Survey Water Supply Paper 1360-B.

RUSSELL, R. H., 1960, *Artificial Recharge of a Well at Walla Walla,* J. Am. Water Works Assoc., v. 52, p. 1427, Nov.

SANFORD, J. H., 1938, *Diffusing Pits for Recharging Water into Underground formations,* J. Am. Water Works Assoc. v. 30, pp. 1755-1766.

SANITARY ENGINEERING RESEARCH LABORATORY, 1955, *Studies in Water Reclamation,* Tech. Bull. 13, Univ. California, Berkeley, 65 pp.

SANITARY ENGINEERING RESEARCH LABORATORY, 1955, *An investigation of Sewage Spreading on Five California Soils,* Tech. Bull. 12, Univ. California, Berkeley, 53 pp.

SAYRE, A. N., and STRINGFIELD, V. T., 1948, *Artificial Recharge of Ground-Water Reservoirs,* J. Am. Water Works Assoc., v. 40, pp. 1152-1158.

SCHIFF, L., 1953, *The Effect of Surface Head on Infiltration Rates Based on the Performance of Ring Infiltrometers and Ponds,* Trans. Am. Geophys. Union, v. 34, pp. 257-266.

SCHIFF, L., 1954, *Water Spreading for Storage Underground,* Agric. Eng., v. 35, pp. 794-800.

SCHIFF, L., 1955, *The Status of Water Spreading for Ground-Water Replenishment,* Trans. Am. Geophys. Union, v. 36, pp. 1009-1020.

SCHIFF, L., 1956, *The Darcy Law in its Selection of Water-Spreading Systems for Ground-Water Recharge,* Symposia Darcy, Internat. Assoc. Sci. Hydrology Pub. no. 41, pp. 99-110.

SCHIFF, L., 1957, *The Use of Filters to Maintain High Infiltration Rates in Aquifers for Ground-Water Recharge,* Internat. Assoc. Sci. Hydrology Pub. no. 44, pp. 217-221.

SCHWARZ, JEHOSHUA, 1967, *Clogging and Contamination of Wells Recharging Lake Kinnereth Water,* TAHAL, P. N. 550, March.

SIGNOR, D. C. and others, 1970, *Annotated Bibliography on Artificial Recharge of Ground Water, 1955-67,* U. S. Geol. Survey Water Supply Paper 1990, 141 pp.

SISSON, W. H., 1955, *Recharge Operations at Kalamazoo,* J. Am. Water Works Assoc., v. 47, pp. 914-922.

SNIEGOCKI, R. T., 1960, *Effects of Viscosity and Temperature — Ground Water Recharge and Conservation,* (discussion), J. Am. Water Works Assoc., v. 52, no. 12.

SNIEGOCKI, R. T., 1963, *Problems in Artificial Recharge through Wells in the Grand Prairie Region Arkansas,* U. S. Geol. Survey Water Supply Paper 1615-E.

SNIEGOCKI, R. T., 1963, *Geochemical Aspects of Artificial Recharge in the Grand Prairie Region, Arkansas,* U. S. Geol. Survey Water Supply Paper 1615-E, 41 pp.

SONDEREGGER, A. L., 1918, *Hydraulic Phenomena and the Effect of Spreading of Flood Water in the San Bernardino Basin, Southern California,* Trans. Am. Soc. Civil Engrs., v. 82, pp. 802-851.

STEINBRUEGGE, G. W. and others, 1954, *Groundwater Recharge by Means of Wells,* Agric. Exp. Sta., Univ. Arkansas, Fayetteville, 119 pp.

STONE, R., and GARBER, W. F., 1952, *Sewage Reclamation by Spreading Basin Infiltration,* Trans. Am. Soc. Civil Engrs., v. 117, pp. 1189-1217.

SUNDSTROM, R. V., and HOOD, H. W., 1952, *Results of Artificial Recharge of the Ground-Water Reservoir at El Paso, Texas,* Texas Board Water Engrs. Bull. 5206, Austin, 19 pp.

SUTER, M., 1956, *High-Rate Recharge of Ground Water by Infiltration,* J. Am. Water Works Assoc., v. 48, pp. 355-360.

SUTER, M., 1956, *The Peoria Recharge Pit: its Development and Results,* Proc. Am. Soc. Civil Engrs., v. 82, no. IR3, 17 pp.

THEIS, C. V., 1941, *The Effect of a Well on the Flow of a Nearby Stream,* Trans. Am. Geophys. Union, 22nd Ann. Meeting, pt. 3.

TIBBETTS, F. H., 1936, *Water-Conservation Project in Santa Clara County,* Trans. Am. Geophys. Union, v. 17, pp. 458-465.

TODD, D. K., 1955, *Ground-Water Flow in Relation to a Flooding Stream,* Proc. Amer. Soc. Civil Engrs. v. 81, sep. 628, 20 pp.

TODD, D. K., 1953, *Annotated Bibliography on Artificial Recharge of Ground Water through 1954,* U. S. Geol. Survey Water Supply Paper 1477, 115 pp.

TODD, D. K., and BEAR, J., 1959, *River Seepage Investigation,* Water Resources Center Contrib. 20, Univ. of California, Berkeley.

TODD, D. K., 1964, *Economics of Ground Water Recharge by Nuclear and Conventional Means,* Rept. UCRL-7850, Lawrence Radiation Laboratory, pp. 1-135, Livermore, Calif., Feb.; also Proc. Am. Soc. Civil Engrs. v. 91, 1965, HY 4, pp. 249-270.

TODD, D. K., 1965, *Nuclear Craters for Ground Water Recharge,* J. Am. Water Works Assoc., v. 57, p. 429, Apr.

TOUPS, J. M., 1969, *Use of Reclaimed Water for Sea Water Intrusion Barrier,* Bull. Calif. Water Pollution Control Assoc., v. 5, no. 3, p. 5.

TRAINER, F. W., and SALVAS, E. H., 1962, *Ground Water Resources of the Massena-Waddington Area, St. Lawrence County, New York, with Emphasis on the Effect of Lake St. Lawrence on Ground Water,* New York Water Res. Comm. Bull. GW-47.

UNKLEBAY, A. G., and COOPER, H. H., Jr., 1946, *Artificial Recharge of Artesian Limestone at Orlando, Florida,* Econ. Geol. v. 41, pp. 293-307.

VALLIANT, J. C., 1962, *Artificial Recharge of Surface Water to the Ogallala Formation in the High Plains of Texas,* High Plains Research Foundation, Bull. 1, 17 pp.

VENHUISEN, K. D., 1967, *The Storage Capacity in the Dunewater Catchment Area of Amsterdam and its Effect on the Water Quality,* Internat. Assoc. Sci. Hydrology, Pub. 72, pp. 109-123.

WALTON, W. C., 1963, *Estimating the Infiltration Rate of a Streambed by Aquifer-Test Analysis,* Internat. Assoc. Sci. Hydrology, Gen. Assembly Berkeley.

WALTON, W. C. and others, 1967, *Recharge from Induced Streambed Infiltration under Varying Groundwater-Level and Stream-Stage Conditions,* Minn. Water Resources Res. Center Bull. 6.

WALTON, W. C., 1969, *Recharge from Induced Streambed Infiltration under Varying Ground-Water Level Conditions,* U. S. Dept. Agric., Agric. Res. Service, ARS-41-147.

WEGENSTEIN, M., 1954, *La recharge de nappes souterraines au moyen de puits centraux et galeries d'alimentation horizontales,* Internat. Assoc. Sci. Hydrology Pub. no. 37, pp. 232-237.

WELSCH, W. F., 1957, *Water Supply Problems in Nassau County, Long Island,* presented at Albany N. Y. at Ann. Convocation of New York Dist. Personnel of Water Resources Div., U. S. Geol. Survey.

WHETSTONE, G. A., 1954, *Mechanism of Ground-Water Recharge,* Agric. Eng., v. 35, pp. 646-647, 650.

WILLIAMS, R. E. and others, 1969, *Feasibility of Reuse of Treated Wastewater for Irrigation, Fertilization and Ground-Water Recharge in Idaho,* Idaho Bur. Mines and Geol. Pamph. 143, 110 pp.

WILSON, L. G., and DE COOK, K. J., 1968, *Field Observations on Changes in the Subsurface Water Regime during Influent Seepage in the Santa Cruz River,* Water Resources Res., v. 4, no. 6, pp. 1219-1235.

WIPPLINGER, O., 1958, *The Storage of Water in Sand; and Investigation of the Properties of Natural and Artificial Sand Reservoirs and of Methods of Developing such Reservoirs,* South West Africa, Windhoek, 107 p.

WITHERSPOON, P. A. and others, 1967, *Interpretation of Aquifer Gas Storage Conditions from Water Pumping Tests,* Am. Gas Assoc. Monogr., New York.

SUB-SURFACE DISPOSAL

AMERICAN PETROLEUM INSTITUTE, 1960, *Subsurface Saltwater Disposal,* API Washington, D. C., 102 pp.

ANONYMOUS, 1966, *Injection Well Earthquake Relationship – Rocky Mountain Arsenal, Denver, Colorado,* Rept. of Inv., U. S. Army Eng. Dist., Omaha Corps of Engrs., Omaha, Neb.

BARRACLOUGH, J. T., 1966, *Waste Injection into a Deep Limestone in Northwestern Florida,* Ground Water, v. 4, no. 1, pp. 22-25.

BERGSTROM, R. E., 1968, *Feasibility of Subsurface Disposal of Industrial Wastes in Illinois,* Ill. Geol. Survey Circ.

BOEGLY, W. J., Jr. and others, 1969, *The Feasibility of Deep-Well Injection of Waste Brine from Inland Desalting Plants,* Office of Saline Water Res. and Dev. Progress Rept. no. 432, U. S. Dept. of the Interior.

CLEARY, E. J., and WARNER, D. L., 1969, *Perspective on the Regulation of Underground Injection of Wastewaters,* Ohio River Valley Water San. Comm., Cincinnati, Ohio.

CLEARY, E. J., and WARNER, D. J., 1970, *Some Considerations in Underground Wastewater Disposal,* J. Am. Water Works Assoc., v. 62, no. 8, p. 489.

DEAN, B. T., 1965, *The Design and Operation of a Deep-Well Disposal System,* J. Water Pollution Control Fed., v. 37, no. 2, pp. 245-254.

DE LAGUNA, WALLACE and others, 1968, *Engineering Development of Hydraulic Fracturing as a Method for Permanent Disposal of Radioactive Wastes,* Oak Ridge Natl. Lab. Rept. no. 4259.

DONALDSON, E. C., 1964, *Subsurface Disposal of Industrial Wastes in the United States,* U. S. Bur. Mines Inf. Circ. 8212, 34 pp.

DRESCHER, W. J., 1965, *Hydrology of Deep-Well Disposal of Radioactive Liquid Wastes,* in *Fluids in Subsurface Environments,* Am. Assoc. Petroleum Geol., Mem. 4, pp. 399-407.

EVERDINGEN, A. F., 1968, *Fluid Mechanics of Deep-Well Disposals,* Am. Assoc. Petroleum Geologists Mem. no. 10, Aug.

FINK, B. E., 1969, *State Regulates Subsurface Waste Disposal in Texas,* Water and Sewage Works, 116, IW-20.

HEALY, J. H. and others, 1968, *The Denver Earthquakes,* Sci., v. 161, no. 3484, p. 1301.

HOLLISTER, J. C., and WEIMER, R. J., 1968, *Geophysical and Geological Studies of the Relationships between the Denver Earthquake and the Rocky Mountain Arsenal Well.,* Pt. A., Colorado School of Mines Quarterly, v. 63, no. 1, Jan.

IVES, R. E., and EDDY, G. E., 1968, *Subsurface Disposal of Industrial Wastes,* Interstate Oil Compact Comm., Oklahoma City, Okla; supplement pub. Jan. 1970.

KOELZER, V. A. and others, 1969, *The Chicago Area Deep Tunnel Project- a Use of the Underground Storage Resource,* J. Water Pollution Control Fed., v. 41, no. 4, Apr.

LEGROS, P. G. and others, 1969, *A Study of Deep Well Disposal of De- salination Brine Waste,* Office of Saline Water Res. and Dev., Progress Rept. no. 456, U. S. Dept of the Interior.

MARSH, J. H., 1968, *Design of Waste Disposal Wells,* Ground Water, v. 6, no. 2, pp. 4-9.

McCLAIN, W. C., 1969, *Disposal of Radioactive Wastes by Hydraulic Fracturing,* Nuclear Eng. Des., v. 9, no. 3, p. 315, also Eng. Index Abs. Jan 1970.

MOSELEY, W., and MALINA, J. F., 1969, *Relationships between Selected Physical Parameters and Cost Responses for the Deep Well Disposal of Aqueous Industrial Wastes,* Water and Wastes Eng., v. 6, no. 9, p. 99.

PARKER, F. L., 1969, *Status of Radioactive Waste Disposal in U. S. A.,* J. San. Eng. Div., Proc. Am. Soc. Civil Engrs., v. 95, p. 439.

PIPER, A. M., 1969, *Disposal of Liquid Wastes by Injection Underground — neither Myth nor Millennium,* Chem. Eng. Progr., v. 65, p. 97.

SELM, R. P., and HULSE, B. T., 1959, *Deep-Well Disposal of Industrial Wastes,* Proc. Purdue Univ. Indus. Waste Conf., pp. 566-586.

SHELDRICK, G. M., 1969, *Deep Well Disposal: are Safeguards being Ig- nored?,* Chem. Eng., v. 76, no. 7, p. 74.

SLAGEL, K. A., and STROGNER, J. M., 1969, *Oil Fields Yield new Deep Well Disposal Technique,* Water and Sewage Works, v. 116, p. 238.

STEWART, R. S., 1968, *Techniques of Deep Well Disposal — a Safe and Efficient Method of Pollution Control,* Proc. 15th Ontario Ind. Waste Conf., Ontario Water Res. Comm., Toronto, Ont.

TALBOT, J. S., 1968, *Some Basic Factors in Consideration and Installation of Deep Well Disposal Systems,* Water and Sewage Works, v. 115, p. 213.

VEIR, B. B., 1969, *Deep Well Disposal Pays off at Celanese Chemical Plant,* Water and Sewage Works, v. 116, no. 5, pp. IW-21.

WARNER, D. L., 1965, *Deep-Well Injection of Liquid Waste,* U. S. Public Health Service Environ. Health Ser. Pub. 999-WP-21, Washington, D. C., 55 pp.

WARNER, D. L., 1967, *Deep Wells for Industrial Waste Injection in the United States — Summary of Data,* Fed. Water Pollution Control Adm. publ. WP-20-10, Washington, D. C., 45 pp.

WARNER, D. L., 1968, *Subsurface Disposal of Liquid Industrial Wastes by Deep Well Injection, in Subsurface Disposal in Geologic Basins — a Study of Reservoir Strata,* Am. Assoc. Petroleum Geol., Mem. 10, pp. 11-20.

WARNER, D. L., 1970, *Regulatory Aspects of Liquid Waste Injection into Saline Aquifers,* J. Water Resources Res., v. 6, no. 5, pp. 1458-1462, Oct.

WESNER, G. M., and BAIER, D. C., 1970, *Injection of Reclaimed Wastewater into Confined Aquifers,* J. Am. Water Works Assoc., v. 62, no. 3, pp. 203-210, Mar.

WRIGHT, J. L., 1969, *Underground Waste Disposal,* Ind. Waste Eng., v. 6, no. 5, p. 24.

BASIN STUDIES AND WATER BALANCES

ACKROYD, E. A. and others, 1967, *Groundwater Contribution to Streamflow and its Relation to Basin Characteristics in Minnesota,* Minn. Geol. Survey Rept. of Invest. 6.

BAKER, D. M., 1950, *Safe Yield of Ground-Water Reservoirs,* General Assembly of Brussels, Internat. Assoc. Sci. Hydrology, v. 2, pp. 160-164.

BANKS, H. O., 1953, *Utilization of Underground Storage Reservoirs,* Trans. Am. Soc. Civil Engrs., v. 118, pp. 220-234.

BOGOMOLOV, G. V., and PLOTNIKOV, N. A., 1956, *Classification des ressources d'eaux souterraines et evaluation de leurs reserves,* Symposia Darcy, Internat. Assoc. Sci. Hydrology, v. 2, pp. 263-271.

BOKE, R. L., and STONER, D. S., 1953, *The Application of Hydrologic Techniques to Ground-Water Problems in California's Central Valley Project,* Proc. Ankara Symp. on Arid Zone Hydrology, UNESCO, Paris, pp. 134-139.

BROWN, C. B., 1944, *Report on an Investigation of Water Losses in Streams Flowing East out of the Black Hills, S. D.,* U. S. Dept. Agr., Soil Conserv. Serv., Sedimentation Sec., Spec. Rept. 8.

BRUNE, GUNNAR, 1970, *How much Underground Water Storage Capacity does Texas Have?* Water Res. Bull., v. 6, no. 4, pp. 588-600.

CLENDENEN, F. B., 1954, *A Comprehensive Plan for the Conjunctive Utilization of a Surface Reservoir with Underground Storage for Basin-Wide Water Supply Development, Solano Project, California,* Ph.D. Eng. thesis, Univ. California, Berkeley, 160 pp.

CLENDENEN, F. B., 1955, *Economic Utilization of Ground Water and Surface Storage Reservoirs,* Paper San Diego, California meeting Am. Soc. Civil Engrs., Feb.

CONKLING, H., 1934, *The Depletion of Underground Water-Supplies,* Trans. Am. Geophys. Union, v. 15, pp. 531-539.

CONKLING, H., 1946, *Utilization of Ground-Water Storage in Stream System Development,* Trans. Am. Soc. Civil Engrs., v. 111, pp. 275-354.

DOLCINI, A. J. and others, 1957, *The California Water Plan,* Bull. 3, Calif. Dept. Water Resources, Sacramento, 246 pp.

FETH, J. H., 1964, *Hidden Recharge,* Ground Water, v. 2, no. 4.

GLEASON, G. B., 1947, *South Coastal Basin Investigation − Overdraft on Ground-Water Basins,* Bull. 53, California Div. Water Resources, Sacramento, 256 pp.

GOLDSCHMIDT, J. J., 1959, *On the Water Balances of Several Mountain Underground Water Catchments in Israel and their Flow Patterns,* Hydrological Service of Israel, Jerusalem, Israel, 10 pp.

HALEY, J. M. and others, 1955, *Santa Clara Valley Investigation,* Bull. 7, California State Water Resources Board, Sacramento, 154 pp.

HITCHON, BRIAN, 1969, *Fluid Flow in the Western Canada Sedimentary Basin. 1. Effect of Topography,* Water Resources Res., v. 5, no. 1, p. 186.

HITCHON, BRIAN, 1969, *Fluid Flow in the Western Canada Sedimentary Basin. 2. Effect of Geology,* Water Resources Res., v. 5, no. 2, p. 460.

HOLLYDAY, E. F., and SEABER, P. R., 1968, *Estimating Cost of Ground-Water Withdrawal for River Basin Planning,* Ground Water, v. 6, no. 4, pp. 15-24.

INGERSON, I. M., 1941, *The Hydrology of Southern San Joaquin Valley, California, and its Relation to Imported Water-Supplies,* Trans. Am. Geophys. Union, v. 22, pp. 20-45.

KAZMANN, R. G., 1951, *The Role of Aquifers in Water Supply,* Trans. Am. Geophys. Union, v. 32, pp. 227-230.

KAZMANN, R. G., 1956, *Safe Yield in Ground Water Development, Reality or Illusion?* Proc. Am. Soc. Civil Engrs., v. 82, no. IR3, 12 pp.

KONOPLYANTSEV, A. A., and KOVALEVSKIY, V. S., 1968, *Ground-Water Regime and Balance Problems in the Soviet Union,* Nature and Resources, v. 4, no. 3, Sept.

LOEHNBERG, ALFRED, 1957, *Water Supply and Drainage in Semi-Arid Countries,* Trans. Am. Geophys. Union, v. 38, no. 4.

LULL, H. M., and MUNNS, E. N., 1950, *Effect of Land Use Practices on Ground Water,* J. Soil and Water Conserv., v. 5, pp. 169-179.

MANN, J. F., 1961, *Factors Affecting the Safe Yield of Ground-Water Basins,* J. Irrigation and Drainage Div., Am. Soc. Civil Engrs., pp. 63-69, Sept.

MCDONALD, H. R., 1955, *The Irrigation Aspects of Ground-Water Development,* Proc. Am. Soc. Civil Engrs., v. 81, sep. 707, 17 pp.

MEINZER, O. E., and STEARNS, N. D., 1928, *A study of Groundwater in the Pomperaug Basin, Connecticut, with Special Reference to Intake and Discharge,* U. S. Geol. Survey Water Supply Paper 597-B.

MEINZER, O. E., 1932, *Outline of Methods for Estimating Ground-Water Supplies,* U. S. Geol. Survey Water Supply Paper 638-C, pp. 99-144.

MEINZER, O. E., 1945, *Problems of the Perennial Yield of Artesian Aquifers,* Econ. Geol. v. 40, pp. 159-163.

MIFFLIN, M. D., 1968, *Delineation of Ground-Water Flow System in Nevada, Desert Res.* Inst. — Univ. of Nevada, Tech. Rept. Series H-W, Hydrology and Water Resources, Publ. no. 4.

RASMUSSEN, W. C., and ANDREASEN, G. E., 1959, *Hydrologic Budget of the Beaverdam Creek Basin, Maryland,* U. S. Geol. Survey Water Supply Paper 1472.

SCHICHT, R. J., and WALTON, W. C., 1961, *Hydrologic Budgets for Three Small Watersheds in Illinois,* Ill. State Water Survey Rept. of Invest. 40.

SIMPSON, T. R., 1952, *Utilization of Ground Water in California,* Trans. Am. Soc. Civil Engrs., v. 117, pp. 923-934.

STRINGFIELD, V. T., 1951, *Geologic and Hydrologic Factors Affecting Perennial Yield of Aquifers,* J. Am. Water Works Assoc., v. 43, pp. 803-816.

SUTCLIFFE, J. V., and RANGELEY, W. R., 1960, *An Estimation of the Long Term Yield of a Large Aquifer at Teheran,* Assembly of Helsinki, Internat. Assoc. Sci. Hydrology, Pub. 52, pp. 264-271.

SWENSON, F. A., 1968, *New Theory of Recharge to the Artesian Basin of the Dakotas,* Bull. Geol. Soc. Am., v. 79, pp. 163-182.

TAYLOR, S., 1964, *The Problem of Groundwater Recharge with Special Reference to the London Basin,* J. Inst. Water Eng., 18, 247-254.

THOMAS, R. O., 1955, *General Aspects of Planned Ground-Water Utilization,* Proc. Am. Soc. Civil Engrs., v. 81, sep. 706, 11 pp.

THORNTHWAITE, C. W., and MATHER, J. R., 1955, *The Water Balance,* Drexel Inst. Techn., Centerton, N. J., 86 pp.

THORNTHWAITE, C. W., and MATHER, J. R., 1955, *The Water Budget and its Use in Irrigation,* in *Water, the Yearbook of Agriculture,* U. S. Dept. of Agric., pp. 346-358.

THORNTHWAITE, C. W., and MATHER, J. R., 1957, *Instructions and Tables for Computing Potential Evapotranspiration and the Water Balance,* Drexel Inst. Techn., Pub. in Climatology, v. 10, no. 3, 311 pp., Centerton, N. J.

THORNWAITE, C. W. and others, 1958, *Three Water Balance Maps of Eastern North America,* Resources for the Future, Inc., Washington, D. C.

TOGH, J., 1970, *A Conceptual Model of the Groundwater Regime and the Hydrogeologic Environment,* J. Hydrology, v. 10, no. 2, pp. 164-176.

TÖTH, J. A., 1962, *A Theory of Ground-Water Motion in Small Drainage Basins in Central Alberta, Canada*, J. Geophys. Res., v. 67, pp. 4375-4387, Oct.

TÖTH, J. A., 1963, *Theoretical Analysis of Groundwater Flow in Small Drainage Basins*, J. Geophys. Res., v. 68.

TROXELL, H. C., 1953, *The Influence of Ground-Water Storage on the Runoff in the San Bernardino and Eastern San Gabriel Mountains of Southern California*, Trans. Am. Geophys. Union, v. 34, pp. 552-562.

TURNER, S. F., and HALPENNY, L. C., 1941, *Ground-Water Inventory in the Upper Gila Valley, New Mexico and Arizona, Scope of Investigation and Methods Used*, Trans. Am. Geophys. Union, v. 22, pp. 738-744.

UBELL, K., 1966, *Investigations into Groundwater Balance by Applying Radioisotope Tracers, Isotopes in Hydrology*, Symp. Vienna, Internat. Atomic Energy Agency, SM 83/36, pp. 521-530.

WALTON, W. C., 1965, *Groundwater Recharge and Runoff in Illinois*, Ill. State Water Survey Rept. of Invest. 48.

WALTON, W. C., 1964, *Potential Yield of Aquifers and Ground Water Pumpage*, J. Am. Water Works Assoc., v. 56, pp. 172-186, Feb.

WALTON, W. C., 1964, *Future Water-Level Declines in Deep Sandstone Wells in Chicago Region*, Ground Water, v. 2, pp. 13-20.

WENTWORTH, C. K., 1951, *The Problem of Safe Yield in Insular Ghyben-Herzberg Systems*, Trans. Am. Geophys. Union, v. 32, pp. 739-742.

WILLIAMS, C. C., and LOHMAN, S. W., 1947, *Methods Used in Estimating the Ground-Water Supply in Wichita, Kansas, Well-Field Area*, Trans. Am. Geophys. Union, v. 28, pp. 120-131.

WILLIAMS, C. C., and LOHMAN, S., 1949, *Geology and Ground-Water Resources of a Part of Southern-Central Kansas, with Special Reference to the Wichita Municipal Water Supply*, Kansas Geol. Survey Bull. 79.

WILLIAMS, R. E., and ALLMAN, D. W., 1969, *Factors Affecting Infiltration and Recharge in a Loess Covered Basin*, J. Hydrology, v. 8, no. 3, July.

WILLIAMS, R. E., 1970, *Groundwater Flow Systems and Accumulation of Evaporite Minerals*, Bull. Am. Assoc. Petroleum Geol., v. 54, no. 7, pp. 1290-1295.

ZEIZEL, A. J. and others, 1962, *Ground-water Resources of DuPage County, Illinois*, Ill. State Water Survey Cooperative Ground-water Rept. 2.

PHREATOPHYTES AND EVAPOTRANSPIRATION

BLANEY, H. F., 1954, *Consumptive Use of Ground Water by Phreatophytes and Hydrophytes,* Internat. Assoc. Sci. Hydrology, General Assembly Rome, Pub. 37, v. 2, pp. 53-62.

CULLER, R. C., 1970, *Water Conservation by Removal of Phreatophytes,* EOS, Trans. Am. Geophys. Union, v. 51, no. 10, Oct.

CRUFF, R. W., and THOMPSON, T. H., 1967, *A Comparison of Methods of Estimating Potential Evapotranspiration from Climatological Data in Arid and Subhumid Environments,* U. S. Geol. Survey Water Supply Paper 1839-M.

HORTON, R. E., 1933, *The Role of Infiltration in the Hydrologic Cycle,* Trans. Am. Geophys. Union, v. 14, pp. 446-460.

JENSEN, M. E., and HAISE, H. R., 1963, *Estimating Evapotranspiration from Solar Radiation,* Proc. Am. Soc. Civil Engrs. J. Irrigation and Drainage Div., v. 89 (IR 4), pp. 15-41.

LEWIS, D. C., and BURGY, R. H., 1964, *The Relationship between Oak Tree Roots and Groundwater in Fractured Rock as Determined by Tritium Tracing,* J. Geophys. Res., v. 69, pp. 2579-2588.

PENMAN, H. L., 1948, *Natural Evapotranspiration from Open Water, Bare Soil, and Grass,* Proc. Roy. Soc. of London, v. 193, pp. 120-145.

PENMAN, H. L., 1956, *Estimating Evapotranspiration,* Trans. Am. Geophys. Union, v. 37, pp. 43-46.

ROBINSON, T. W., 1958, *Phreatophytes,* U. S. Geol. Survey Water Supply Paper 1423, 84 pp.

ROBINSON, T. W., and JOHNSON, A. I., 1961, *Selected Bibliography on Evaporation and Transpiration,* U. S. Geol. Survey Water Supply Paper 1539-R, 25 pp.

ROBINSON, T. W., 1970, *Evapotranspiration by Woody Phreatophytes in the Humboldt River Valley near Winnemucca, Nevada,* U. S. Geol. Survey Prof. Paper 491-D.

SIBBONS, J. L. H., 1962, *A Contribution to the Study of Potential Evapotranspiration,* Geografiska Annaler, v. 44, pp. 279-292.

SMITH, G. E. P., 1924, *The Effect of Transpiration of Trees on the Ground-water Supply* (abstract), J. Wash. Acad. Sci., v. 14.

TANNER, C. B., and PELTON, W. L., 1960, *Potential Evapotranspiration Estimates by the Approximate Energy Balance Method of Penman,* J. Geophys. Res., v. 65, pp. 3391-3413.

WHITE, W. N., 1932, *A Method of Estimating Ground-Water Supplies Based on Discharge by Plants and Evaporation from Soil, Results of Investigations in Escalante Valley, Utah,* U. S. Geol. Survey Water Supply Paper 659-A.

BASE FLOW AND BANK STORAGE

BARNES, B. S., 1939, *The Structure of Discharge Recession Curves,* Trans. Am. Geophys. Union, v. 20, pp. 721-725.

CHERNAYA, T. M., 1964, *Comparative Evaluation of Graphical Methods of Separation of Ground-Water Components of Streamflow Hydrographs,* Soviet Hydrology, v. 5, pp. 454-465.

CROSS, W. P., and HEDGES, R. E., 1959, *Flow Duration of Ohio Streams,* Ohio Div. of Water Bull. 31.

GRUNDY, F., 1951, *The Ground-Water Depletion Curve, its Construction and Uses,* General Assembly of Brussels, Internat. Assoc. Sci. Hydrology, v. 2, pp. 213-217.

HALL, F. R., 1968, *Base-Flow Recessions – a Review,* Water Resources Res., v. 4, no. 5, pp. 973-983.

HOUK, I. E., 1921, *Rainfall and Runoff in the Miami Valley,* State of Ohio, Miami Conserv. Dist. Tech. Repts., pt. VIII.

ISIHARA, T., and TAGAKI, F., 1965, *A Study on the Variation of Low Flow,* Disaster Prevention Res. Inst., Kyoto, Japan, Bull. 95, pp. 75-98.

KNISEL, Jr., and WALTER, G., 1963, *Baseflow Recession Analysis for Comparison of Drainage Basins and Geology,* J. Geophys. Res., v. 68, no. 12.

KUNKLE, G. R., 1962, *The Base Flow-Duration Curve, a Technique for the Study of Groundwater Discharge from a Drainage Basin,* J. Geophys. Res. v. 67, no. 4.

KUNKLE, G. R., 1965, *Computations of Ground-Water Discharge to Streams during Floods or to Individual Reaches during Baseflow, by Use of Specific Conductance,* U. S. Geol. Survey Prof. Paper 525-D, pp. 207-210.

LANGBEIN, W. B., 1940, *Some Channel Storage and Unit Hydrograph Studies,* Trans. Am. Geophys. Union, v. 21, pp. 620-627.

MENDENHALL, W. C., 1905, *The Hydrology of San Bernardino Valley, California,* U. S. Geol. Survey Water Supply Paper 142.

MERRIAM, C. F., 1948, *Ground-Water Records in River-Flow Forecasting,* Trans. Am. Geophys. Union, v. 29, pp. 384-386.

MERRIAM, C. F., 1951, *Evaluation of Two Elements Affecting the Characteristics of the Recession Curve,* Trans. Am. Geophys. Union, v. 32, pp. 597-600.

MEYBOOM, P., 1961, *Estimating Ground-Water Recharge from Stream Hydrographs,* J. Geophys. Res., v. 66, no. 4.

PINDER, G. F., and JONES, J. F., 1969, *Determination of the Ground-Water Component of Peak Discharge from the Chemistry of Total Runoff,* Water Resources Res., v. 5, no. 2, p. 438.

PIPER, A. M. and others, 1939, *Geology and Groundwater Hydrology of the Mokelumne Area, California,* U. S. Geol. Survey Water Supply Paper 780.

POGGE, E. C., 1968, *Effects of Bank Seepage on Flood Hydrographs,* Kansas State Univ. Water Resources Res. Inst. Proj. Completion Rept., Contrib. no. 33.

SINGH, K. P., 1968, *Some Factors Affecting Base Flow,* Water Resources Res. v. 4, no. 5, pp. 985-999.

SINGH, K. P., 1969, *Theoretical Baseflow Curves,* J. Hydraulics Div., Am. Soc. Civil Engrs., v. 95, no. HY6, Nov.

SNYDER, W. M., 1968, *Subsurface Implications from Surface Hydrograph Analysis,* Proc. Second Seepage Symp., Phoenix, Arizona.

VISOCKY, A. P., 1970, *Estimating the Ground-Water Contribution to Storm Runoff by the Electrical Conductance Method,* Ground Water, v. 8, no. 2, pp. 5-11.

WERNER, P. W., and SUNDQUIST, K. J., 1951, *On the Ground-Water Recession Curve for Large Watersheds,* Gen. Assembly Brussels, Internat. Assoc. Sci. Hydrology, v. 2, pp. 202-212.

GROUND-WATER MODELS

ARAVIN, V. I., 1941, *Experimental Investigation of Unsteady Flow of Ground Water* (in Russian), Trans. Sci. Res. Inst. Hydrotechnics, USSR, v. 30, pp. 79-88.

BABBITT, H. E., and CALDWELL, D. H., 1948, *The Free Surface around, and Interference between, Gravity Wells,* Univ. Ill. Bull., v. 45, no. 30.

BATURIC-RUBCIC, J., 1969, *The Study of Nonlinear Flow through Porous Media by Means of Electrical Models,* J. of Hydraulic Res., v. 7, no. 1, Delft, The Netherlands.

BAUMANN, PAUL, 1951, *Ground-Water Movement Controlled through Spreading,* Proc. Am. Soc. Civil Engrs. v. 77, sep. no. 86.

BEAR, J., 1960, *Scales of Viscous Analogy Models for Ground Water Studies,* J. Hydraulics Div. Am. Soc. Civil Engrs., pp. 11-23, Feb.

BEDINGER, M. S. and others, 1970, *Methods and Applications of Electrical Simulation in Ground-Water Studies in the Lower Arkansas and Verdigris River Valleys, Arkansas and Oklahoma,* U. S. Geol. Survey Water Supply Paper 1971, 71 pp.

BENNETT, G. D. and others, 1968, *Electric-Analog Studies of Brine Coning beneath Fresh-Water Wells in the Punjab Region, West Pakistan,* U. S. Geol. Survey Water Supply Paper 1608.

BERMES, B. J., 1960, *An Electric Analog Model for Use in Quantitative Studies,* U. S. Geol. Survey Mimeographed Rept.

BOTSET, H. G., 1946, *The Electrolytic Model and its Application to the Study of Recovery Problems,* Trans. Am. Inst. Min. and Metal. Engrs. v. 165, pp. 15-25.

BOUWER, H., 1962, *Analyzing Ground-Water Mounds by Resistance Network,* J. Irrigation and Drainage Div. Am. Soc. Civil Engrs., pp. 15-36, Sept.

BREDEHOEFT, J. D. and others, 1966, *Inertial and Storage Effects in Well-Aquifers Systems, an Analog Investigation,* Water Resources Res., v. 2, no. 4, pp. 697-707.

CHILDS, E. C. and others, 1953, *The Measurement of the Hydraulic Permeability of Saturated Soil in Situ,* pt. 2, Proc. Roy. Soc. London, ser. A, v. 216, no. 1124.

d'ANDRIMONT, R., 1905, *Note préliminaire sur une nouvelle méthode pour étudier expérimentalement l'allure des nappes aquifères dans les terrains permeables en petit,* Annales Soc. Geol. Belgique, v. 32, Liége, pp. M115-M120.

d'ANDRIMONT, R., 1906, *Sur la circulation de l'eau des nappes aquifères contenues dans des terrains permeables en petit,* Annales, Soc. Geol. Belgique, v. 33, Liége, pp. M21-M33.

DAY, P. R., and LUTHIN, J. N., 1954, *Sand-Model Experiments on the Distribution of Water-Pressure under an Unlined Canal,* Proc. Soil Sci. Soc. Am., v. 18, no. 2.

DEBRINE, B. E., 1970, *Electrolytic Model Study for Collector Wells under River Beds,* J. Water Resources Res., v. 6, no. 3, p. 971-978.

DE JONG, G. DE JOSSELIN, 1961, *Moire Patterns of the Membrane Analogy for Groundwater Movement Applied to Multiple Fluid Flow,* J. of Geophys. Res., v. 66, pp. 3625-3628.

DE JONG, G. DE JOSSELIN, 1962, *Electrische analogie modellen voor het oplossen van geo-hydrologische problemen,* Water, v. 46, pp. 43-45.

DE JONG, G. DE JOSSELIN, 1962, *Een eenvoudige methode voor het nabootsen van een oneindig potentiaalveld,* Water, v. 46, pp. 185-186.

DE WIEST, R. J. M., 1962, *Free Surface Flow in Homogeneous Porous Medium,* Trans. Am. Soc. Civil Engrs., v. 127, Chapt. I, pp. 1045-1089.

DIETZ, D. N., 1941, *Een modelproef ter bestudeering van niet-stationnaire bewegingen van het grondwater,* Water, v. 25, The Hague, pp. 185-188.

DIETZ, D. N., 1944, *Ervaringen met modelonderzoek in de hydrologie,* Water, v. 28, The Hague, pp. 17-20.

EDELMAN, J. H., 1947, *Over de berekening van grondwater-stroomingen,* Doctorate thesis, Delft Tech. Univ. Netherlands, 77 pp.

FELIUS, G. P., 1954, *Recherches hydrologiques par des modèles électriques,* Gen. Assembly Rome, Internat. Assoc. Sci. Hydrology v. 2, pp. 162-169.

GUNTHER, E., 1940, *Lösung von Grundwasseraufgaben mit Hilfe der Strömung in dünnen Schichten,* Wasserkraft und Wasserwirtschaft, v. 3, no. 3, pp. 49-55.

GUNTHER, E., 1940, *Untersuchung von Grundwasserströmungen durch analoge Strömungen zäher Flüssigkeiten,* Forschung auf dem Gebiete des Ingenieur-wesens, v. 11, pp. 76-88.

HANSEN, V. E., 1952, *Complicated Well Problems Solved by the Membrane Analogy,* Trans. Am. Geophys. Union, v. 33, pp. 912-916.

HARDER, J. A. and others, 1953, *Laboratory Research on Sea Water Intrusion into Fresh Ground-Water Sources and Methods of its Prevention-Final Report,* Sanitary Eng. Research Lab., Univ. California, Berkeley, 68 pp.

HELE-SHAW, H. S., 1897, *Experiments on the Nature of the Surface Resistance in Pipes and on Ships,* Trans. Inst. Naval Architects, v. 39, pp. 145-156.

HELE-SHAW, H. S., 1898, *Investigation of the Nature of Surface Resistance of Water and of Stream-Line Motion under Certain Experimental Conditions,* Trans. Inst., Naval Architects, v. 40, pp. 21-46.

HELE-SHAW, H. S., 1899, *Stream-Line Motion of a Viscous Film,* Rept. 68th Meeting British Assoc. for the Advancement Sci., pp. 136-142.

HERBERT, ROBIN, 1968, *Analyzing Pumping Tests by Resistance Network Analogue,* Ground Water, v. 6, no. 2, pp. 12-19.

HERBERT, ROBIN, 1968, *Time Variant Ground-Water Flow by Resistance Network Analogues,* J. Hydrology, v. 6, pp. 237-264.

HERBERT, ROBIN, 1970, *Modelling Partially Penetrating Rivers on Aquifer Models,* Ground Water, v. 8, no. 2, pp. 29-37.

HORNER, W. L., and BRUCE, W. A., 1950, *Electrical-Model Studies of Secondary Recovery,* in *Secondary Recovery of Oil in the United States,* 2nd ed., Am. Petroleum Inst., Washington, D. C., pp. 195-203.

HUBBERT, M. K., 1937, *Theory of Scale Models as Applied to the Study of Geologic Structures,* Bull. Geol. Soc. Am., v. 48, pp. 1456-1520.

HURST, W., 1941, *Electrical Models as an Aid in Visualizing Flow in Condensate Reservoirs,* The Petroleum Engr., v. 12, no. 10, pp. 123-124, 127, 129.

IRMAY, S., 1964, *Theoretical Models of Flow through Porous Media,* Rilem Symp. on the Transfer of Water in Porous Media, Paris, April 7-10.

JENKINS, C. T., 1968, *Electric-Analog and Digital-Computer Model Analysis of Stream Depletion by Wells,* Ground Water, v. 6, no. 6, pp. 27-35.

JOHNSON, A. L., 1963, *Selected References on Analog Models for Hydrologic Studies,* App. F, Proc. Symp. on Transient Ground Water Hydraulics, Colorado State Univ., July 25-27.

KARPLUS, W. J., 1958, *Analog Simulation,* McGraw-Hill Book, Co. Inc., New York.

KASHEF, A. I. and others, 1952, *Numerical Solutions of Steady-State and Transient Flow Problems,-Artesian and Water-Table Wells,* Purdue Univ. Eng. Exp. Sta. Bull. 117, Lafayette Ind., 116 pp.

KIMBLER, O. K., 1970, *Fluid Model Studies of the Storage of Freshwater in Saline Aquifers,* J. Water Resources Res., v. 6, no. 5, pp. 1522-1527, Oct.

KIRKHAM, D., 1940, *Pressure and Streamline Distribution in Waterlogged Land Overlying an Impervious Layer,* Proc. Soil Sci. Soc. Am., v. 5, pp. 65-68.

KORN, G. A., and KORN, T. M., 1952, *Electronic Analog Computers,* McGraw Hill Book Co. Inc., New York.

KRAYENHOFF VAN DE LEUR, D. A., 1962, *Some Effects of the Unsaturated Zone on Non-Steady Free-Surface Groundwater Flow as Studied in a Scaled Granular Model,* J. Geophys. Res., v. 67, pp. 4347-4362, Oct.

KRUL, W. F. J. M., and LIEFRINCK, F. A., 1946, *Recent Ground-Water Investigations in the Netherlands,* Elsevier Publishing Co., New York, 78 pp.

LAU, L. and others, 1958, *Studies of Flow Dispersion in Porous Media,* San. Eng. Res. Lab. Rept. no. 4, IER ser. 93, Univ. of California, Berkeley.

LEE, B. D., 1948, *Potentiometric-Model Studies of Fluid Flow in Petroleum Reservoirs,* Trans. Am. Inst. Min. and Metal. Engrs., v. 174, pp. 41-66.

LIEBMANN, G., 1950, *Solution of Partial Differential Equations with a Resistance Network Analogue,* British J. of Applied Physics, v. 1, pp. 92-103.

LIEBMANN, G., 1954, *Resistance Network Analogues with Unequal Meshes or Sub-Divided Meshes,* British J. of Applied Physics, v. 5, pp. 362-366.

LUTHIN, J. N., 1953, *An Electrical Resistance Network Solving Drainage Problems,* Soil Sci., v. 75, pp. 259-274.

LUTHIN, J. N., and GASKELL, R. A., 1950, *Numerical Solution for Tile Drainage of Layered Soils,* Trans. Am. Geophys. Union, v. 31, pp. 595-602.

MEIN, R. G., and TURNER, A. K., 1968, *A Study of the Drainage of Irrigated Sand Dunes Using an Electrical Resistance Analogue,* J. Hydrology, v. 6, no. 1, Jan.

MOORE, A. D., 1949, *Fields from Fluid Flow Mappers,* J. Appl. Phys. v. 20.

MOULDER, E. A., and JENKINS, C. T., 1969, *Analog-Digital Models of Stream-Aquifer Systems,* Ground Water, v. 7, no. 5, pp. 19-25.

MUSKAT, M., 1949, *The Theory of Potentiometric Models,* Trans. Am. Inst. Min. and Metal. Engrs., v. 179, pp. 216-221.

MUSKAT, M., 1935, *Seepage of Water through Dams with Vertical Faces,* Physics, v. 6.

NAOR, I., and BEAR, J., 1963, *Model Investigations of Coastal Ground-Water Interception,* TAHAL, Tel-Aviv, Israel, 54 pp.

OPSAL, F. W., 1955, *Analysis of Two-and Three-Dimensional Ground-Water Flow by Electrical Analogy,* The Trend in Eng. at the Univ. Washington, v. 7, no. 2, Seattle, pp. 15-20, 32.

PINDER, G. F., and BREDEHOEFT, J. D., 1968, *Application of the Digital Computer for Aquifer Evaluation,* Water Resources Res., v. 4, no. 5, pp. 1069-1095.

PRICKETT, T. A., 1967, *Designing Pumped Well Characteristics into Electric Analog Models,* Ground Water, v. 5, no. 4.

PRICKETT, T. A., and LONNQUIST, C. G., 1968, *Comparison between Analog and Digital Simulation Techniques for Aquifer Evaluation,* Symp. of Tucson, Arizona, Internat. Assoc. Sci. Hydrology.

ROBINOVE, C. J., 1962, *Ground-Water Studies and Analog Models,* U. S. Geol. Survey Circ. 468, 12 pp.

RUSHTON, K. R., and BANNISTER, R. G., 1970, *Aquifer Simulation on Slow Time Resistance-Capacitance Networks,* Ground Water, v. 8, no. 4.

SAMMEL, E. A., 1963, *Evaluation of Numerical-Analysis Methods for Determining Variations in Transmissivity,* Internat. Assoc. Sci. Hydrology Pub. no. 64, Subterranean Waters, pp. 239-251.

SANTING, G., 1951, *Infiltratie en modelonderzoek,* Water, v. 35, no. 21, pp. 234-238, no. 22, pp. 243-246, The Hague.

SANTING, G., 1951, *Modèle pour l'étude des problèmes de l'écoulement simultane des eaux souterraines douces et saluées,* General Assembly of Brussels, Internat. Assoc. Sci. Hydrology, v. 2, pp. 184-193.

SANTING, G., 1957, *A Horizontal Scale Model, Based on the Viscous Flow Analogy, for Studying Ground-Water Flow in an Aquifer Having Storage,* General Assembly of Toronto, Internat. Assoc. Sci. Hydrology, pp. 105-114.

SANTING, G., 1958, *Recente ontwikkelingen op het gebied van de spleetmodellen voor het onderzoek van grondwaterstromingen,* Water, no. 15, July.

SCHICHT, R. J., 1965, *Ground-Water Development in East St. Louis Area, Illinois,* Ill. State Water Survey Rept. of Invest. 51.

SEMCHINOVA, M. M., 1953, *Comparison of Experimental Data with Theory for the Case of Unsteady Flow Located on a Horizontal Water Table* (in Russian) Inghenerny Sbornik, Inst., Mech., Acad. Sci., USSR, v. 15, pp. 195-200.

SHAW, F. S., and SOUTHWELL, R. V., 1941, *Relaxation Methods Applied to Engineering Problems, VII, Problems Relating the Percolation of Fluids through Porous Materials,* Proc. Royal Soc., Ser. A, v. 178, pp. 1-17.

SKIBITZKE, H. E., 1961, *Electronic Computers as an Aid to the Analysis of Hydrologic Problems,* Internat. Assoc. Sci. Hydrology Pub. 52.

STALLMAN, R. W., 1956, *Use of Numerical Methods for Analyzing Data on Ground Water Levels,* Symposia Darcy, Internat. Assoc. Sci. Hydrology Pub. 41, pp. 227-231.

STALLMAN, R. W., 1963, *Calculation of Resistance and Error in an Electric Analog of Steady Flow through Nonhomogeneous Aquifers,* U. S. Geol. Survey Water Supply Paper 1544G.

STALLMAN, R. W., 1963, *Electric Analog of Three-Dimensional Flow to Wells and its Application to Unconfined Aquifers,* U. S. Geol. Survey Water Supply Paper 1536-H, pp. 205-242.

STALLWORTH, T. W., 1950, *Quickly Constructed Model Facilitates Seepage Studies,* Civil Eng., v. 20, no. 7, pp. 45-46.

STERNBERG, Y., and SCOTT, V., 1963, *The Hele-Shaw Model as a Tool in Ground-Water Research,* Natl. Water Well Assoc. Conf., San Francisco, Sept.

TODD, D. K., 1954, *Unsteady Flow in Porous Media by Means of a Hele-Shaw Viscous Fluid Model,* Trans. Am. Geophys. Union, v. 35, pp. 905-916.

TODD, D. K., 1955, *Flow in Porous Media Studied in Hele-Shaw Channel,* Civil Eng., v. 25, no. 2, p. 85.

TODD, D. K., 1956, *Laboratory Research with Ground-Water Models,* Symposia Darcy, Internat. Assoc. Sci. Hydrology, Pub. 41, pp. 199-206.

VAIDHIANATHAN, V. I. and others, 1934, *A Hydrodynamical Investigation of the Subsoil Flow from Canal Beds by Means of Models,* Proc. Indian Acad. Sci., sec. A, v. 1.

VAN EVERDINGEN, R. O., and BHATTACHARYA, B. K., 1963, *Data for Ground-Water Model Studies,* Geol. Survey of Canada, Paper 63, 31 pp.

VREEDENBURGH, C. G. J., and STEVENS, O., 1936, *Electric Investigation of Underground Water Flow Nets,* Proc. Internat. Conf. Soil Mech. and Foundation Eng., v. 1, Harvard Univ., Cambridge, Mass., pp. 219-222.

WALTON, W. C., and NEILL, J. C., 1960, *Analyzing Groundwater Problems with Mathematical Models and a Digital Computer,* Internat. Assoc. Sci. Hydrology Pub. 52.

WALTON, W. C., and WALKER, W. H., 1961, *Evaluation of Wells and Aquifers by Analytical Methods,* J. Geophys. Res. v. 66, no. 10.

WALTON, W. C., and PRICKETT, T. A., 1963, *Hydrogeologic Electric Analog Computers,* J. Hydraulics Div. Am. Soc. Civil Engrs., pp. 67-91, Nov.

WALTON, W. C., 1964, *Electric Analog Computers and Hydrogeologic System Analysis in Illinois,* Ground Water, v. 2, no. 4.

WALTON, W. C., and ACKROYD, E. A., 1966, *Effects of Induced Streambed Infiltration on Water Levels in Wells during Aquifer Tests,* Minn. Water Resources Res. Center, Bull. 2.

WALTON, W. C., 1966, *Pre-Feasibility Report on Chicago Tunnel Drainage Project,* typewritten report prepared for Harza Engineering Co., Chicago, Ill.

WERNER, P. W., and NOREN, D., 1951, *Progressive Waves in Non-Artesian Aquifers,* Trans. Am. Geophys. Union, v. 32, no. 2.

WILLIAMS, D. E., 1966, *Viscous Model Study of Ground-Water Flow in a Wedge-Shaped Aquifer,* Water Resources Res., v. 2, no. 3, pp. 479-495.

WOLF, A., 1948, *Use of Electrical Models in Study of Secondary Recovery Projects,* The Oil and Gas J., v. 46, no. 50, pp. 94-98.

WORSTELL, R. V., and LUTHIN, J. N., 1959, *A Resistance Network Analog for Studying Seepage Problems,* Soil Science, v. 88, pp. 267-269.

WYCKOFF, R. D. and others, 1932, *Flow of Liquids through Porous Media under the Action of Gravity,* Physics, v. 3.

WYCKOFF, R. D., and REED, D. W., 1935, *Electrical Conduction Models for the Solution of Water Seepage Problems,* Physics, v. 6, pp. 395-401.

YANG, S., 1949, *Seepage Toward a Well Analyzed by the Relaxation Method,* Ph.D. thesis, Harvard Univ., Cambridge, Mass.

ZANGER, C. N., 1953, *Theory and Problems of Water Percolation,* U. S. Bur. Reclamation Eng. Mon. 8.

ZEE, C. H., 1955, *Flow into a Well by Electric and Membrane Analogy,* Proc. Am. Soc. Civil Engrs., v. 81, sep. 817, 21 pp.

LAND SUBSIDENCE

BULL, W. B., 1961, *Causes and Mechanics of Near-Surface Subsidence in Western Fresno County, California,* U. S. Geol. Survey Prof. Paper 424-B, pp. 187-189.

DAVIS, G. H. and others, 1963, *Land Subsidence Related to Decline of Artesian Pressure in the Ocala Limestone at Savannah, Georgia,* Eng. Geol. Case Histories, Geol. Soc. Am., v. 4.

DOMENICO, P. A., and MIFFLIN, M. D., 1965, *Water from Low-Permeability Sediments and Land Subsidence,* Res. Assoc., Desert Res. Inst. Univ. Nevada Pub., v. 1, no. 4.

DOMENICO, P. A., and CLARK, G., 1964, *Electric Analogs in Time-Settlement Problems,* Proc. Am. Soc. Civil Engrs. 90 (SM3).

GIBBS, H. J., 1960, *A Laboratory Testing Study of Land Subsidence,* Proc. Pan Am. Conf. Soil Mech. Foundation Eng. 1st, Mexico City, 1959, v. 1.

GILLULY, JAMES, and GRANT, U. S., 1949, *Subsidence in the Long Beach Harbor Area, California,* Bull. Geol. Soc. Am., v. 60, pp. 461-530.

GREEN, J. H., 1964, *The Effect of Artesian-Pressure Decline on Confined Aquifer Systems and its Relation to Land Subsidence,* U. S. Geol. Survey Water Supply Paper 1779-T, 11 pp.

GREEN, J. H., 1962, *Compaction of the Aquifer System and Land Subsidence in the Santa Clara Valley, California,* U. S. Geol. Survey Prof. Paper 450-D, art. 172, pp. D175-D178.

INTERNATIONAL ASSOCIATION OF SCIENTIFIC HYDROLOGY/ UNESCO, 1969, *Land Subsidence,* Proc. Tokyo Symp. Sept. 1969, Composite: English/French, v. 1, 324 pp., v. 2, 337 pp. (UNESCO Studies and Reports in Hydrology, 8).

JOHNSON, A. I. and others, 1968, *Physical and Hydrologic Properties of Water-Bearing Deposits in Subsiding Areas in Central California,* U. S. Geol. Survey Water Supply Paper 497-A.

LOEHNBERG, ALFRED, 1958, *Aspects of the Sinking of Mexico City and Proposed Countermeasures,* J. Am. Water Works Assoc., v. 50, no. 3, pp. 432-440, Mar.

LOFGREN, B. E., 1961, *Measurement of Compaction of Aquifer Systems in Areas of Land Subsidence,* U. S. Geol. Survey Prof. Paper 424-B, art. 24.

LOFGREN, B. E., and KLAUSING, R. L., 1969, *Land Subsidence due to Ground-Water Withdrawal, Tulare Wasco Area, California,* U. S. Geol. Survey Prof. Paper 437-B.

LOHMAN, S. W., 1961, *Compression of an Elastic Artesian Aquifer,* U. S. Geol. Survey Prof. Paper 424-B.

MEADE, R. H., 1968, *Compaction of Sediments Underlying Areas of Land Subsidence in Central California,* U. S. Geol. Survey Water Supply Paper 497-D.

MILLER, R. E., 1961, *Compaction of an Aquifer System Computed from Consolidated Tests and Decline in Artesian Head,* U. S. Geol. Survey Prof. Paper 424-B, B54-B58.

PIERCE, R. L., 1970, *Reducing Land Subsidence in the Wilmington Oil Field by Use of Saline Waters,* J. Water Resources Res., v. 6, no. 5, pp. 1505-1514, Oct.

POLAND, J. F., and DAVIS, G. H., 1956, *Subsidence of the Land Surface in the Tulare-Wasco (Delano) and Los Banos-Kettleman City Area, San Joaquin Valley, California,* Trans. Am. Geophys. Union, v. 37, pp. 287-295.

POLAND, J. F., 1960, *Land Subsidence in the San Joaquin Valley, California, and its Effect on Estimates of Ground-Water Resources,* Internat. Assoc. Sci. Hydrology Pub. 52, pp. 324-335.

POLAND, J. F., 1961, *The Coefficient of Storage in a Region of Major Subsidence Caused by Compaction of an Aquifer System,* U. S. Geol. Survey Prof. Paper 424-B.

POLAND, J. F., and GREEN, J. H., 1962, *Subsidence in the Santa Clara Valley, California, a Progress Report,* U. S. Geol. Survey Water Supply Paper 1619-C.

PROKOPOVICH, N. P., and MAGLEBY, D. C., 1968, *Land Subsidence in Pleasant Valley Area, Fresno County, California,* J. Am. Water Works Assoc., v. 60, p. 413, Apr.

ROLL, J. R., 1967, *Effect of Subsidence on Well Fields,* J. Am. Water Works Assoc., v. 59, p. 80, Jan.

TOLMAN, C. F., and POLAND, J. F., 1940, *Ground-Water Salt-Water Infiltration and Ground-Surface Recession in Santa Clara Valley, Santa Clara County, California,* Trans. Am. Geophys. Union, 21st Ann. Meeting pt. 1.

WIER, W. W., 1950, *Subsidence of Peat Lands of the Sacramento-San Joaquin Delta, California,* Hilgardia, v. 20, pp. 37-56.

WILSON, G., and GRACE, H., 1942, *The Settlement of London due to Under-Drainage of the London Clay,* J. Inst. Civil Engrs. v. 19, no. 2.

WINSLOW, A. G., and DOYEL, W. W., 1954, *Land-Surface Subsidence and its Relation to the Withdrawal of Ground Water in the Houston-Galveston Region, Texas,* Econ. Geol. v. 49, pp. 413-422.

ZEEVAERT, LEONARDO, 1963, *Foundation Problems Related to Ground Surface Subsidence in Mexico City,* in *Field Testing of Soils,* Am. Soc. for Testing and Materials Special Pub. no. 322, pp. 57-66.

GROUND WATER LAW

ANONYMOUS, 1967, *Water Law Atlas,* State Bur. of Mines and Mineral Resources, New Mexico Inst. of Mining and Technology, Socorro, N. M., Circ. 95.

BLACK, A. P., 1947, *Basic Concepts in Ground Water Law,* J. Am. Water Works Assoc., v. 39, pp. 989-1002.

BLISS, J. H., 1951, *Administration of the Ground-Water Law of New Mexico,* J. Am. Water Works Assoc. v. 43.

CONKLING, H., 1937, *Administrative Control of Underground Water: Physical and Legal Aspects,* Trans. Am. Soc. Civil Engrs., v. 102, pp. 753-837.

CRITCHLOW, H. T., 1948, *Policies and Problems in Controlling Ground-Water Resources,* J. Am. Water Works Assoc. v. 40, pp. 775-783.

DEUTSCH, M., 1963, *Ground-Water Contamination and Legal Controls in Michigan,* U. S. Geol. Survey Water Supply Paper 1691, 79 pp.

ELY, NORTHCUTT, 1963, *Legal Problems in Development of Water Resources,* 57th Meeting of Princeton Univ. Conference, pp. 89-94.

FOOD AND AGRICULTURE ORGANIZATION OF THE UNITED NATIONS, 1964, *Groundwater Legislation in Europe,* FAO Legislative Series no. 5, 175 pp.

HARDING, S. T., 1936, *Water Rights for Irrigation,* Stanford Univ. Press, Stanford, Calif. 176 pp.

HARDING, S. T., 1953, *United States Water Law,* Trans. Am. Soc. Civil Engrs., v. CT, pp. 343-356.

HARDING, S. T., 1955, *Statutory Control of Ground Water in the Western United States,* Trans. Am. Soc. Civil Engrs., v. 120, pp. 490-498.

HUGHES, W. F., 1945, *Proposed Ground-Water Conservation Measures in Texas,* Texas J. Sci., v. 2, pp. 35-45.

HUTCHINS, W. A., 1942, *Selected Problems in the Law of Water Rights in the West,* U. S. Dept. Agric. Misc. Pub. 418, 513 pp.

HUTCHINS, W. A., 1946, *The Hawaiian System of Water Rights*, Bd. of Water Supply of Honolulu.

HUTCHINS, W. A., 1955, *Trends in the Statutory Law of Ground Water in the Western States*, Texas Law Review, v. 34, pp. 157-191.

HUTCHINS, W. A., 1955, *The New Mexico Law of Water Rights*, State Engineer of New Mexico (in cooperation with U. S. Dept. of Agr.).

HUTCHINS, W. A., 1956, *Irrigation Water Rights in California*, Agric. Exp. Sta. Circ. 452, Univ. of California, Berkeley, 56 pp.

HUTCHINS, W. A., 1956, *The California Law of Water Rights*, State Calif., Sacramento, 571 pp.

JACOBSTEIN, J. M., and MERSKY, R. M., 1966, *Water Law Bibliography 1847-1965*, Jefferson Law Book Co., Silver Spring, Maryland.

KIERSCH, G. A., 1969, *The Geologist and Legal Cases — Responsibility, Preparation and the Expert Witness*, in *Legal Aspects of Geology in Engineering Practice*, Geol. Soc. Am. Eng. Case Histories, no. 7, pp. 1-6.

McGUINNESS, C. L., 1945, *Legal Control of Use of Ground Water*, Water Works Eng., v. 98, pp. 475, 508, 510, 512.

McGUINNESS, C. L., 1951, *Water Law with Special Reference to Ground Water*, U. S. Geol. Survey Circ. 117, 30 pp.

NATIONAL RESOURCES PLANNING BOARD, 1943, *State Water Law in the Development of the West*, Water Resources Committee, Subcommittee on State Water Law, Washington, D. C., 138 pp.

NATIONAL WATER WELL ASSOCIATION, 1970, *Bibliography of State Well Drilling Laws*, Nat. Water Well Assoc., Columbus, Ohio.

NATIONAL WATER WELL ASSOCIATION, 1970, *Model Law for Proper Regulation of the Well Drilling Business*, Nat. Water Well Assoc., Columbus, Ohio.

O'BYRNE, J. C., 1956, *Symposium-Water Use and Control*, Iowa Law Review, v. 41, no. 2, Iowa City, Iowa.

PIPER, A. M., 1959, *Requirements of a Model Water Law*, J. Am. Water Works Assoc. v. 51.

PIPER, A. M., and THOMAS, H. E., 1958, *Hydrology and Water Law — What is Their Future Common Ground?*, in *Water Resources and the Law*, Univ. Michigan Law School.

PIPER, A. M., 1960, *Interpretation and Current Status of Ground-Water Rights,* U. S. Geol. Survey Circ. 432.

PRESIDENT'S WATER RESOURCES POLICY COMMISSION, 1950, *Water Resources Law,* v. 3, Washington, D. C., 777 pp.

STATE OF CALIFORNIA, 1951, *Water Code,* Sacramento, 756 pp.

THOMAS, H. E., 1955, *Water Rights in Areas of Ground-Water Mining,* U. S. Geol. Survey Circ. 347, 16 pp.

THOMAS, H. E., 1958, *Hydrology vs. Water Allocation in the Eastern United States,* in *The Law of Water Allocation in the Eastern United States,* The Ronald Press Co., New York.

THOMAS, H. E., 1961, *Ground Water and the Law,* U. S. Geol. Survey Circ. 446, 6 pp.

THOMAS, H. E., 1970, *Water Laws and Concepts,* U. S. Geol. Survey Circ. 629.

THOMPSON, D. G., and FIEDLER, A. G., 1938, *Some Problems Relating to Legal Control of Use of Ground Waters,* J. Am. Water Works Assoc., v. 30, pp. 1049-1091.

TOLMAN, C. F., and STIPP, A. C., 1941, *Analysis of Legal Concepts of Subflow and Percolating Waters,* Trans. Am. Soc. Civil Engrs., v. 106, pp. 882-933.

MANAGEMENT AND CONSERVATION

ALLISON, S. V., 1967, *Cost, Precision, and Value Relationships of Data Collection and Design Activities in Water Development Planning,* Calif. Water Resources Center Contrib. 120, 142 pp., Berkeley, Calif.

AMERICAN SOCIETY OF CIVIL ENGINEERS, 1961, *Ground Water Basin Management,* Manual of Engineering Practice no. 40, 160 pp.

ANONYMOUS, 1956, *Water Use in the United States, 1900-1975,* Supplement to Willing Water 38, Am. Water Works Assoc. 8 pp.

BANKS, H. O., 1960, *Priorities for Water Use,* Proc. Natl. Conf. on Water Pollution, pp. 153-156, 179, 181, U. S. Public Health Service, Washington, D. C.

BARKSDALE, H. C., and REMSON, IRWIN, 1954, *The Effect of Land Management Practices on Ground Water,* Internat. Assoc. Sci. Hydrology, General Assembly Rome, Pub. 37, v. 2, pp. 520-525.

BATELLE MEMORIAL INSTITUTE, 1966, *Bibliography on Socio-Economic Aspects of Water Resources,* Contract no. 14-01-0001-822, U. S. Office of Water Resources Res., 453 pp.

BEAR, J., and LEVIN, O., 1967, *The Optimal Yield of an Aquifer, Artificial Recharge and Management of Aquifers,* Proc. Symposium of Haifa, Internat. Assoc. Sci. Hydrology, Pub. 72.

BITTINGER, M. W., 1964, *The Problem of Integrating Ground Water and Surface Water Use,* Ground Water, v. 2, no. 3, July.

BREDEHOEFT, J. D., and YOUNG, R. A., 1970, *The Temporal Allocation of Ground Water – a Simulation Approach,* Water Resources Res., v. 6, no. 1, p. 3.

BURAS, N., 1963, *Conjunctive Operation of Dams and Aquifers,* J. Hydraul. Div., Proc. Am. Assoc. Civil Engrs., v. 89, no. HY6, pp. 111-131, Nov.

BURAS, N., and BEAR, J., 1964, *Optimal Utilization of a Coastal Aquifer,* Proc. VIth Internat. Congr. of Agric. Engrs., Lausanne, Switzerland, Sept.

BURAS, N., 1966, *Dynamic Programming in Water Resources Development,* in *Advances in Hydroscience,* ed. by Ven Te Chow, v. 3, Academic Press, New York, pp. 367-412.

BURDICK, C. B., 1942, *Ground Water – A Vital National Resource, Midwest Problems,* J. Am. Water Works Assoc., v. 37.

BURT, O. R., 1964, *Optimal Resource Use over Time with an Application to Groundwater,* Management Sci., v. 11, pp. 80-93.

BURT, O. R., 1966, *Economic Control of Groundwater Reserves,* J. Farm. Econ., 48, 632-647.

BURT, O. R., 1967, *Temporal Allocation of Groundwater,* Water Resources Res., v. 3, no. 1, pp. 45-56.

CHUN, R. Y. D. and others, 1964, *Optimum Conjuctive Operation of Ground Water Basins,* J. Hydraul. Div., Proc. Am. Soc. Civil Engrs. v. 90, no. HY4, pp. 79-95.

CHUN, R. Y. D. and others, 1966, *Planned Utilization of Ground Water Basins, Coastal Plain of Los Angeles County, Operation and Economics,* Bull. 104, Appendix C, Dept. of Water Resources, Sacramento, Calif.

COHEN, PHILIP and others, 1968, *An Atlas of Long Island's Water Resources,* New York Water Resources Bull. 62.

CRAWFORD, N. H., and LINSLEY, R. K., 1966, *Digital Simulation in Hydrology: Stanford Watershed Model IV,* Tech. Rept. no. 39, Dept. Civil Eng., Stanford Univ., Calif.

DOMENICO, P. A., 1968, *Optimal Ground-Water Mining,* Water Resources Res., v. 4, no. 2, pp. 247-255, Apr.

DORFMAN, R. and others, 1965, *Waterlogging and Salinity in the Indus Plain: Some Basic Considerations,* Harvard Univ. Water Resources Reprint no. 77.

DRACUP, J. A., 1966, *The Optimum of a Ground-Water and Surface Water System: A Parametric Linear Programming Approach,* Water Resources Center, Contrib. no. 107, Univ. of California, Berkeley, July.

ESHETT, A., and BITTINGER, M. W., 1965, *Stream-Aquifer System Analysis,* J. Hydraul. Div., Proc. Am. Soc. Civil Engrs., v. 91, no. HY6, pp. 153-164, Nov.

FALK. L. H., 1970, *Economic Aspects of Ground-Water Basin Control,* Louisiana Water Resources Res. Inst. Bull. GT-3, Louisiana State Univ., Baton Rouge, La.

FIERING, M., 1967, *A Groundwater-Precipitation Model for Streamflow Synthesis,* Proc. IBM Sci. Computing Symp. on Water and Air Resource Management, Yorktown Heights, N. Y., pp. 203-213, Oct. 23-25.

FOOSE, R. M., 1951, *Ground-Water Conservation and Development,* Monthly Bull., Penn. Dept. Internal Affairs, Harrisburg, v. 19, no. 2, pp. 17-28.

FOWLER, L. C., 1964, *Ground Water Management for the Nation's Future – Ground Water Basin Operation,* J. Hydraul. Div., Proc. Am. Soc. Civil Engrs., v. 90, no. HY4, pp. 51-57, July.

HALL, W. A., and DRACUP, J. A., 1967, *The Optimum Management of Groundwater Resources,* Proc. Internat. Conf. on Water for Peace, Washington, D. C., May 23-31.

HANSEN, H. J., 1970, *Zoning Plan for Managing a Maryland Coastal Aquifer,* J. Am. Water Works Assoc., v. 62, no. 5, May.

KAZMANN, R. G., 1958, *Problems Encountered in the Utilization of Ground-Water Reservoirs,* Trans. Am. Geophys. Union, v. 39, pp. 94-99.

KELSO, M. M., 1961, *The Stock Resource Value of Water,* J. Farm Econ., v. 43, no. 5, pp. 112-1129, Dec.

KISIEL, C. C., and DUCKSTEIN, L., 1968, *Water Resources Development and Management in the Tucson Basin,* Paper presented at 1968 Spring Joint ORSA/TIMS meeting, May 1-3, San Francisco, Calif.

KUDELIN, B. I., 1957, *The Principles of Regional Estimation of Underground Water Natural Resources and the Water Balance Problem,* Internat. Assoc. Sci. Hydrology, General Assembly Toronto, Pub. 44, v. 2, pp. 150-167.

LEOPOLD, L. B., 1958, *Water and the Conservation Movement,* U. S. Geol. Survey Circ. 402.

LOHMAN, S. W., 1953, *Sand Hills Area, Nebraska,* in *Sub-Surface Facilities of Water Management and Patterns of Supply — Type Area Studies,* U. S. Congress, House of Rep., Interior and Insular Affairs Comm., pp. 79-91.

MANN, J. F., Jr., 1968, *Concepts in Ground Water Management,* J. Am. Water Works Assoc., v. 60, p. 1336, Dec.

MANN, J. F., Jr., 1969, *Ground-Water Management in the Raymond Basin, California,* in *Legal Aspects of Geology in Engineering Practice,* Geol. Soc. Am. Eng. Geology Case Histories, no. 7, pp. 61-74.

MANNING, J. C., 1967, *Resume of Ground Water Hydrology in the Southern San Joaquin Valley,* J. Am. Water Works Assoc., v. 59, pp. 1513-1526, Dec.

MAXEY, G. B., and DOMENICO, P. A., 1967, *Optimum Development of Water Resources in Desert Basins,* Am. Water Resources Assoc., Proc. Ser. 4, Symp. on Groundwater Hydrology, San Francisco, pp. 84-90.

McGUINNESS, C. L., 1946, *Recharge and Depletion of Ground-Water Supplies,* Proc. Am. Soc. Civil Engrs., v. 72, pp. 963-984.

McMILLAN, W. D., 1966, *Theoretical Analysis of Groundwater Basin Operations,* Water Resources Center Contrib. no. 114, Univ. of California, Berkeley, Nov.

MILLER, D. W., 1958, *The Ground-Water Phase of Well Field Management,* TAPPI, v. 41, no. 10, pp. 174A-178A.

MURRAY, C. R., 1968, *Estimated Use of Water in the United States, 1965,* U. S. Geol. Survey Circ. 556, 53 pp.

NACE, R. L., 1960, *Water Management, Agriculture, and Ground-Water Supplies,* U. S. Geol. Survey Circ. 415, 12 pp.

NACE, R. L., 1965, *Global Thirst and the International Hydrological Decade,* J. Am. Water Works Assoc., v. 57, no. 7.

NELSON, A. G., and BRUSH, C. D., 1967, *Cost of Pumping Irrigation Water in Central Arizona,* Ariz. Agr. Exp. Sta., Tech. Bull. 182, p. 48.

OWEN, L. W., 1968, *Ground Water Management and Reclaimed Water,* J. Am. Water Works Assoc., v. 60, no. 2, pp. 135-144, Feb.

PARKER, G. G. and others, 1964, *Water Resources of the Delaware River Basin,* U. S. Geol. Survey Prof. Paper 381, 200 pp.

PORTER, N. W., 1941, *Concerning Conservation of Underground Water with Suggestions for Control,* Trans. Am. Soc. Heat. Vent. Engrs. v. 47, pp. 309-322.

RENSHAW, E. F., 1963, *The Management of Ground Water Reservoirs,* J. Farm Econ., v. 45, no. 2, pp. 285-295.

ROCKAWAY, J. D., and JOHNSON, R. B., 1967, *Statistical Analysis of Ground Water Use and Replenishment,* Tech. Rept. no. 2, Water Resources Res. Center, Purdue Univ., Lafayette, Indiana, Sept.

STULTS, H. M., 1966, *Predicting Farmer Response to a Falling Water Table: an Arizona Case Study,* Conf. Proc., Comm. Econ. Water Resources of the Western Agric. Econ. Research Council, Rept. no. 15, Las Vegas, Nevada, Dec.

SUTER, M. and others, 1959, *Preliminary Report on Ground Water Resources of the Chicago Region,* Ill. State Water Survey and Geol. Survey Cooperative Ground-water Rept. 1.

THEIS, C. V., 1940, *The Source of Water Derived from Wells, Essential Factors Controlling the Response of an Aquifer to Development,* Civil Engineering, May.

THOMAS, H. E., and SCHNEIDER, W. J., 1970, *Water as an Urban Resource and Nuisance,* U. S. Geol. Survey Circ. 601-D.

TYSON, H. N., and WEBER, E. M., 1964, *Ground-Water Management for the Nation's Future — Computer Simulation of Ground-Water Basins,* J. Hydraul. Div., Proc. Am. Soc. Civil Engrs., v. 90, no. HY4, pp. 59-77, July.

UPSON, J. E., 1967, *Plans of the U. S. Geological Survey Water Resources Division for Research Investigations and Data Collection in Ground-water,* Ground Water, v. 5, no. 2.

WALTON, W. C., 1964, *Potential Yield of Aquifers and Ground Water Pumpage in Northeastern Illinois,* J. Am. Water Works Assoc., Feb.

WELSCH, W. F., 1960, *Ground Water Recharge and Conservation — Conservation in Nassau County, Long Island, N. Y.,* J. Am. Water Works Assoc., v. 52, p. 1494, Dec.

WESCHLER, L. F., 1968, *Water Resources Management: the Orange County Experience,* California Govt. Ser. no. 14, Inst. Govt. Affairs, Univ. of California, Davis, Jan.

WIENER, A., 1967, *The Role of Advanced Techniques of Ground Water Management in Israel's National Water Supply System,* Bull. Internat. Assoc. Sci. Hydrology, v. 12, no. 2, pp. 32-38.

WOODS, P. C., 1967, *Management of Hydrologic Systems for Water Quality Control,* Water Resources Center, Contrib. no. 121, Univ. of California, Berkeley, June.

EDUCATION AND TRAINING

AGNEW, A. F., 1968, *The Geological Profession and Ground Water,* Ground Water, v. 6, no. 1, pp. 5-9.

BEAR, J., 1969, *Hydrologic Education in Israel,* Internat. Seminar for Hydrology Professors, Urbana, 13-25 July, Preprint 23 pp.

DE WIEST, R. J. M., 1964, *Educational Facilities in Ground-Water Hydrology and Geology,* Ground Water, v. 2, pp. 18-24.

EATON, E. D., 1969, *Comments on some Recent Trends in Hydrology Research,* Internat. Seminar for Hydrology Professors, Urbana, 13-25 July, Preprint, 21 pp.

EVANS, D. D., and HARSHBARGER, J. W., 1969, *Curriculum Development in Hydrology,* Internat. Seminar for Hydrology Professors, Urbana, 13-25 July, Preprint, 20 pp.

HARSHBARGER, J. W., and FERRIS, J. G., 1963, *Inter-Disciplinary Training Program in Scientific Hydrology,* Ground Water, v. 1, no. 2.

KINDSVATER, C. E., and SNYDER, W. M., 1969, *Hydrologic Training for Water Resources Development,* Internat. Seminar for Hydrology Professors, Urbana, 13-25 July, Preprint, 12 pp.

MEYBOOM, P., 1969, *Some Aspects of the Scientific Communication System in Hydrology,* Ground Water, v. 7, no. 4, pp. 28-37.

MOORE, W. L., 1969, *Teaching Aids in Hydrology,* Internat. Seminar for Hydrology Professors, Urbana, 13-25 July, Preprint, 18 pp.

UNIVERSITIES COUNCIL ON WATER RESOURCES, 1967, *Education in Hydrology, United States Universities, early 1966,* Water Resources Center, Univ. of California, Los Angeles, 44 pp.

WALTON, W. C., 1964, *Education Facilities in Ground-Water Geology and Hydrology in the United States and Canada – 1963,* Ground Water, v. 2, no. 3.

WATER WITCHING

ELLIS, A. J., 1917, *The Divining Rod-a History of Water Witching,* U. S. Geol. Survey Water Supply Paper 416, 59 pp.

EMMART, B. D., 1952, *All-Purpose Dowsing,* Atlantic Monthly, v. 190, no. 1, pp. 90-92.

RIDDICK, T. M., 1952, *Dowsing – an Unorthodox Method of Locating Underground Water Supplies or an Interesting Facet of the Human Mind,* Proc. Am. Philosophical Soc., v. 96, pp. 526-534.

ROBERTS, KENNETH, 1951, *Henry Gross and his Dowsing Rod,* Doubleday and Co., Garden City, N. Y.

RYDER, L. W., 1949, *The Case for Water Witching,* J. New England Water Works Assoc., v. 63, pp. 232-237.

VOGT, E. Z., and HYMAN, R., 1959, *Water Witching U. S. A.,* Univ. of Chicago Press, 259 pp.

ZIEMKE, P. C., 1949, *Water Witching,* Water and Sewage Works, v. 96, p. 136.